Sex
with Paula Yates

PAULA YATES

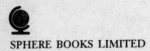

SPHERE BOOKS LIMITED

Sphere Books Limited
27 Wrights Lane, London W8 5TZ

First published in Great Britain by
Sphere Books Ltd 1987

The author is grateful for permission to use an extract from
Portnoy's Complaint by Philip Roth, which was
kindly granted by Jonathan Cape Ltd, 32 Bedford Square,
London WC1B 3EL

TRADE
MARK

Set in 11/13pt Linotron Ehrhardt

Printed and bound in Great Britain by Collins

- How many times a day is normal?
- Can I have sex now that I am pregnant?
- I ate a dodgy Chinese last night and was ill. My friend says I could get pregnant. Is she right?
- I have not grown very tall, nor have I got much body hair. Does this mean I am not going to be a very sexy man?

Contents

Intro   ix

1   Love's raging torment   1

2   The dawn of time   15

3   How to be cute   35

4   Parents   51

5   What actually happens   61

6   Contraception   77

7   The family way   95

8   Wanking is bad for you and other myths   119

9   Angst, angst and yet more angst   129

10   Clap   149

11   Yet more horrible problems   165

Communications – Addresses/Telephone numbers   175

Intro

I was inspired to begin this book when I realised that there was still an amazing number of people who believed that you couldn't get pregnant if you were standing up, it was your first time, you jumped up and down afterwards, or on the third Thursday in February if it was a Leap Year. This all started me thinking about doing a slim volume that would at least go part of the way to putting people's minds at rest. However, it was not as easy as I had anticipated, mainly because huge holes in my own knowledge suddenly emerged. And I had to resort to reading a mountainous pile of sex manuals instead of having my usual afternoon nap.

The first one gave an in-depth description of how to bring a woman to orgasm under a table in a restaurant, using only your big toe! Another one suggested that the way to make a man feel like The Only Man On Earth was to kneel before him whispering 'I worship your penis,' at his knob. In the interests of in-depth research, I actually tried this and was greeted with complete derision.

I was also ably assisted by two of my girlfriends. One of them, who wishes to remain anonymous for reasons that you will grasp as you read on, volunteered invaluable information. Her immense curiosity, about the whole subject made fieldwork a pleasure for her. On one occasion, she entranced the young man who came to fix her Potterton boiler by alluringly grabbing his spanner and on another, proved that not all Arabs are big gift givers when one that had been wooing her for some weeks (unsuccessfully), passionately presented her with a Gucci bottle opener. So my heartfelt thanks must go to my anonymous friend for her invaluable assistance in venturing into regions where I would have required six pairs of knickers and a shot of Novocaine.

A huge portion of this book will seem rather like a sexual version of the manual for a Ford Fiesta. But that's because it's impossible to write a book about how to fall in love. You will hopefully do that first and this book will be the icing on the cake. Without wishing to sound too like Barbara Cartland, being madly in love makes everything different.

1 *Love's raging torment*

There comes a point in everyone's life when they ask themselves one simple question, 'Who on earth is ever going to fuck me if I carry on looking like this?' The truth is that just about everybody has somebody who thinks they're gorgeous. No matter what you think, there *is* somebody for everybody, and a good chance that you'll meet them.

It is still quite rare for teenagers to feel alluring. This is because during one's teenage years everyone's body goes through a transformation that has all the subtlety of a Page Three Girl. One day, you're a delightful cross between Milly Molly Mandy and Anne of Green Gables and the next, you're a heady combination of Gina Lollobrigida and Madonna. One minute, you've got a figure like Seb Coe and the next, your entire body appears to have reconstructed itself in sago. *There are bits there that were not there last time you looked*! All of a sudden, for both boys and girls, it's like having to get used to somebody else's body living in your clothes.

The other major problem is skin. A skin that only weeks before might have resembled a peach, prepares itself for a big night out by erupting like Vesuvius. One look in the mirror confirms the belief that you might as well have Pizza Hut stamped on the back of your neck. Another fact of life is that spots travel. One of the few pleasures to be had from spots is, of course, squeezing them in front of the mirror so that the guck hits it at high velocity. However, guck inevitably ends up on fingers and, quite mystifyingly, the spot that was on your nose this morning is a boil on the bottom by lunch.

All of this *angst* manifests itself in having to spend many

solitary hours alone, surrounded by old socks, underpants
and copies of *Razzle*, looking into the mirror. The more you
look, the worse it gets. The more you look, the more you
wonder who on earth is ever going to want to kiss you, let
alone anything else. You imagine contemporaries that you
fancy being held at gunpoint and, when given the choice of
kissing you or eating a snot sandwich, they inevitably opt for
the latter. The only thing about this is that everyone else feels
the same way. Everyone thinks that they're never going to
meet anyone, and the prettiest girl in the class is no more

confident that anyone else. In the privacy of her bedroom she's in front of the mirror too.

All this leads to a miserable feeling, 'I am ugly, I am fat, I am spotty, life's a hollow sham. I am never going out again. I am going to stay in with my Leonard Cohen records forever.' Girls may groan 'Morten from Aha wouldn't look at me twice.' Men will weigh up the dismal chances of Grace Jones grooving the night away in their arms. Console yourself with the thought that neither Grace Jones nor Morten from Aha are likely to be at Shakers in Croydon tonight anyway. It is also a medically proven fact that the first thing women look at when they walk into a crowded room is men's crotches, followed by their faces. So lads, unless you happen to have a gigantic zit poking through the front of your Levi 501s, your secret should be safe for at least a few minutes.

Pleasant as it is to wallow in unadulterated self-pity and self-loathing, it is not the greatest route to a hot social life, and those of you who wish to become the Peter Stringfellow of the local youth club may find it hard to do from the back bedroom of a semi-detached in Bolton. I realise that everyone thinks that they look so hideous there is no point in even bothering, but the best thing to do is gird your loins and go for it. Nightclubs are notoriously dark anyway and you can be guaranteed every other girl is wondering when God's going to provide her with the boobs for her boob tube and every boy is stoically resolving not to dance in case his mates laugh at him. Teenagers are not only the most self-conscious people on earth but also sometimes the cruellest.

'Everyone would say that they were doing it. They'd say they'd done it with some girl, and then you'd take her out and she wouldn't shag you. You didn't want to accuse the bloke of not having done it, in case it was just you she didn't fancy.'

If one were a fly on the wall in the common room of any Upper Sixth at break-time, one might imagine that the entire student population has a sex life that's a torrid rival to Sylvia Kristel or Warren Beatty's. In fact, the ones who claim to be doing it with the gardener, the entire Second XI and the head boy are inevitably at home with an old John Taylor poster. Cliché that it is, it's the quiet ones you've got to watch.

The problem is that nobody wants to admit that they've never done It (or that nobody's ever asked them) and everybody's bursting to know what It's like. For teenagers, a sex life sometimes seems like a passport to a life of sophistication – rather like a Duran Duran video – when in fact, handled unwisely, it can become yet another nightmare to add to exams, parents, spots, flab and the worry of whether you're ever going to get a job.

If you lose your virginity simply because you think you are the last person in your class to do so, you may ironically find that you are the first. Losing one's virginity is a major milestone in life, even though at times it may feel like a millstone round your neck and you can't wait to get rid of it. The important thing about the decision to lose it is to make that decision for yourself and for your own motives, rather than because you feel you are being pressurised by your contemporaries. Better motives are being in love, or feeling a great passion for someone. It's better to remember that sex is meant to be sexy and not a competitive sport. You may feel that everyone around you is doing it but they're probably not, so the best thing to do is divide everything your friends tell you they are doing by five and treat the rest like a whopper anyway.

There are enormous amounts of pros and cons to be weighed up. The first thing to do is to be entirely honest with yourself, even if you're finding it hard to be entirely honest with your friends. You must ask yourself clearly *why* are you doing this and if you are satisfied that it's because you want to, then you're another step closer to being happier about the whole thing. The next step is to avoid feeling in some way cheap, dirty or cast aside like a used toilet tissue afterwards. You don't want to feel like you've been used in any way.

After working out your own motives, the second most important thing to sort out is contraception. Do not imagine that because you haven't prepared yourself sensibly with contraception you are in some way a Good Girl who didn't anticipate sex. That sort of Good Girl all too often ends up a pregnant girl. She is also a stupid girl. The worst thing that can possibly happen to you is to get pregnant because you were too embarrassed or couldn't be bothered to get contraception. It's no good going round thinking 'It can't happen to me,' and despite massive coverage of it being also the man's responsibility, it would be foolish to imagine that contraception is something that boys think about automatically. To be brutally honest, boys don't think about it. Boys think about getting laid. Boys also don't get pregnant. Therefore, if you are planning to embark upon your lovelife it is a wise move to get some form of contraception with which you are happy, and not rely upon other people to look after you. If you are not able to talk to your doctor or your parents, which – let's face it – lots of people aren't, there is an index at the back of this book which gives the addresses of sympathetic, unshockable and discreet people who are used to helping people like you every day.

The first time

One of the things many people ask the first time they make love is 'Is that it?' or 'Was that it?' They are astounded to discover that not only did the earth not move, it didn't even twitch. Heavy petting can often feel, especially for girls, a lot sexier than actually making love initially. You may even wonder why people bother? Even more gripping, you will now be able to look at people on the bus and think 'Oh, my God, do they do that?' You may even start to look a little strangely at your parents across the breakfast table and try to imagine your mother doing the Dance of the Seven Veils around the divan in her pink Bri-nylon Baby Dolls.

Boys may be disappointed because it doesn't last very long and girls may be disappointed to discover that it can hurt and that the experienced boyfriend they thought they had was a quivering wreck when it came to making love. Sex does get better with practice and, like riding a bicycle, it's something you never forget how to do. But it's also a bit like expecting to be able to play like Yehudi Menuhin after your first violin lesson.

The disappointed feeling does fade. You will stop thinking 'What were all the great romantic novelists going on about and is Barbara Cartland talking through her bum?' You will stop wondering what Juliet saw in Romeo, what Heloise saw in Abelard or even Christie in Billy. You will notice, however, that all of these are great love affairs. The operative word being love. Love makes all the difference when it comes to sex. There are worse motives for having sex the first time than plain curiosity. It's natural to wonder what it actually feels like – but then it's natural to wonder what scuba diving feels like and you wouldn't do that without getting the right equipment first! But love is the best aphrodisiac of all.

Questions and answers

Q My boyfriend says if I don't sleep with him, he's going to chuck me. What should I do?

A Sex is not something you should ever be blackmailed into doing. Sex is something you do because you love someone, not because they're going to leave you if you don't join in. If a boy truly likes you, he must unfortunately realise that he has to respect your feelings, whether or not he agrees with them and no matter how

6

frustrated he's getting. It's tough shit but that's the score. Everyone's mother, if they even suspect you're about to die from a broken heart, always says 'There's plenty more fish in the sea, dear.' And mothers have an annoying tendency to be right about things like that. The other thing to remember about being chucked is that for a short while afterwards your ex-boyfriend will suddenly seem like the only boy on earth you could have ever loved. If you allow yourself to wallow in that you will start to doubt yourself and your decisions when, in fact, you made a wise one. If the only thing he was interested in was getting you into bed, regardless of what you wanted, the chances are he wasn't very grown-up. And making love's a very grown-up thing to do. If *you* don't think you're ready, then you're definitely not.

Q Why is my mother so worried about me going into my bedroom with my girlfriend to play records?

A The first thing about being a parent is that one almost always imagines the worst. Your parents are saddled with the burden of loving you more than anyone else in the world, and this automatically magnifies any worries that they might have to what must seem like ludicrous proportions to you. In any dealings with parents, the best thing to do, if you can manage it, is to put yourself in their slippers. Imagine your mother's sitting in the kitchen with her *Woman's Own*, three eccles cakes and a cup of tea, and you slink in with a nubile girlfriend and say you're going upstairs to play records. Ten minutes later, mater hears the pounding strains of Prince apparently regurgitating several meals. What does she imagine? Not that you're sitting there reading the sleeve notes and fondling the free poster! She casts her mind back to the happy hours she spent with your dad (hard as this may be to visualise).

She's bound to think you're kissing at the very least. She knows that emotions can be aroused suddenly and one thing leads to another. What started as a Prince record session can result in a lot of Smutty Business. But you'd be surprised; she's probably not so much worried that you are actually going to make love, as that your girlfriend might get pregnant. She wants to know you're being responsible but she's almost certainly too embarrassed to confront you with anything. So she ends up by just being stroppy. If there's any way you can put her mind at rest – perhaps by speaking to your dad – it will make everyone's lives much happier.

Q My mother has asked me if I want to go on the Pill. I don't. What should I say?

A One of the things about this generation is that you are the children of a very liberal generation of parents. The chances are that in the 1960s your parents were preaching free love and 'swinging'. One of the main things about growing up is that you rebel against your parents' values automatically, even if it's only for a while. You may well be a lot more prim than your mum, but it still makes questions like this very embarrassing. Your mum probably imagines that you're planning to make love soon. Whether you are or not, it's always embarrassing when your parents make any kind of enquiries into your private life, because there comes a point when your life *is* private in certain respects. Don't get offended, just be grateful that you are able to talk about those things if ever you should need to. One day, when you do decide to make love for the first time, it will be a lot easier to deal with the question of contraception if your mum is on your side.

Q My boyfriend and I have been 'making love' with all our underwear on. Is there any chance I could get pregnant?

A This is very inventive of you – but not absolutely safe. If your boyfriend comes anywhere near your piddler, you could become pregnant. Y-fronts are not particularly well-known for their contraceptive qualities or you'd never be able to get near the underwear counter in Marks & Spencer.

Q Will it hurt the first time?

A It is perfectly normal for it to hurt unless you're a boy, in which case it's pretty unusual. Unless you are totally relaxed and in a comfortable environment – which does not include behind the bike sheds, the back seat of a Cortina or, as in the case of my friend, on the stairs with a clear view out of the window so he could spot his parents coming home – you can easily be hurt and bruised. It's best to make love the first time in the most comfortable situation you can arrange, which may not be easy but it will be worth it.

If you're trying to get it all over with in a hurry, your body is unlikely to be ready. Women produce a natural lubricant which makes them wet and the whole business much easier. If you're not wet enough, you're not ready and that's when it's most likely to hurt. The more it hurts, the tenser you will get. If you are nervous, worried or frightened you will be less likely to get sexually aroused. Sex is meant to be sexy and unless you feel sexy it might be better to wait until another time. (Your boyfriend may put up some resistance to this.)

Q What is a hymen?

A This is also known as a maidenhead, which you may have thought was a small town in Berkshire but has actually been in your knickers all this time. The entrance to a girl's vagina is partly blocked by a layer of skin called the hymen. Hymens, like fingernails, are usually enormously easy to break and this can happen in a number of ways, including horse riding, gym and using Tampax. If you haven't got one, it doesn't mean you're not a virgin.

Q Will I bleed?

A When a girl has sex for the first time, if her hymen hasn't broken already, it's not uncommon for it to bleed a little. Boys often think that if a girl didn't bleed, she wasn't a virgin. This is a load of crap. Sometimes, instead of breaking the skin, it simply stretches and then only some slight discomfort will result. There's almost bound to be a twinge of pain and this might well take away from some of the pleasure, but it's quickly over with and shouldn't hurt so much the second time. And by the third time, you may even be thinking of taking it up as a hobby.

Q Will it fit?

A Boys may worry that their stupendous willies won't fit in. So may some girls. Here, I can put your mind at rest. Basically, any willie will fit inside any girl provided she's relaxed enough. (If there are any boys who have found this not to be the case, could they please write to my friend Josephine.)

Q I came after three seconds – is there something wrong with me?

A No. Between three and five seconds seems to be about the average for boys the first time. This is because you may have spent fifteen years waiting for it and it feels very nice. It is also a shock after all those hours in the darkened bedroom with Leonard Cohen to have found somebody who is willing to do it with you – not just willing but

probably delighted. All of this is a bit much for the system. But very soon you will get used to it and by the end of the week you may be up to twenty-three seconds.

Q It was stupid. Am I normal?

A You may wonder what the great romantic novelists have been wittering on about. As I said earlier, what did Juliet see in Romeo, what did Eloise see in Abelard, or Cleopatra in Antony? When you are in love, 'it' tends to be different. When you are in love, everything is different. And sex won't seem stupid, it will seem splendid. You don't have to be in love, but it's a whole different ball game when you are.

Q What is the most important thing about losing your virginity?

A Having made the decision to make love for the first time, the most important thing to remember may seem mundanely practical and very unromantic. It is contraception. No matter what else you may be thinking of, once you have made the decision to make love, contraception is the number one priority, far more important than finding somewhere to do it. In chapter five we describe all the methods of contraception available to you, and where to get hold of them. But remember, embarrassing as it may seem to you, if you are adult enough to consider yourself ready to make love, you are adult enough to take responsibility for your actions. To get pregnant simply because you have ignored contraception is about the most stupid thing you can do. It can't be stressed enough how crucial this is. You might be frightened to talk to your doctor or your parents or even your friends about this, but don't imagine that lack of contraception is going to stop people making love. Once you've decided to do it, you'll probably go straight ahead.

Q Can I get pregnant the first time?

A Yes.

Q Can I get pregnant from heavy petting?

A The answer, surprisingly, is yes. If both of you have your clothes off, you have to be very careful. Like spots, sperm travel and it only takes one to make you pregnant.

Q What is safe?

A Kissing, hugging and cuddling. Watching television is remarkably safe – provided you do it with all your clothes on. You cannot get pregnant by giving someone a blow job. (For 'What Is A Blow Job', see chapter nine).

Q I'm frightened to tell my girlfriend that I'm a virgin. She thinks I've got bags of experience.

A If she has bags of experience, she might be able to tell. But chances are that even if she guesses, it won't matter to her anyway. If she has plenty of experience, she will probably enjoy showing you what to do. If you are both virgins, the best thing you can do is get some contraception and get on with it.

Q Can my boyfriend tell if I'm not a virgin?

A Boys like to think they can – but then boys like to think a lot of things. As we've said, some girls bleed the first time but many, many more don't, because their hymen has already been broken. Sex is one of our most basic and natural instincts, so you will know what to do even if you haven't done it before. Obviously, you're not going to be swinging off the chandeliers but neither are you going to be completely useless. Nature takes over somewhere along the way, with a vengeance.

Q Is it important to be a virgin?

A Unless you want to become the Princess of Wales – and Diana seems to have pipped you to the post there – no. However, if you have decided to remain a virgin for personal reasons (and they must be your reasons, not your parents' or your friends') you may find it a hard decision to keep, because you will be under pressure – from your own body, from your boyfriend and from simply looking around you; the media are constantly telling us that everybody's doing it to everyone, regardless of age, status, or religious beliefs. These are the pressures you will be under. If it is important to you to be a virgin, then stay one. But don't do it for anyone else.

Q Does it matter if I don't have a boyfriend or a girlfriend?

A No, it doesn't. It is, however, important to have friends – of both sexes. A boy can be a friend as much as another girl (and *vice versa*). But I think it's very important to remember the unique value of a special girlfriend if you are a girl. It's never worth falling out with your special and close friends over boyfriends who may only last two weeks. Not getting on with other girls is an unpleasant trait which should be stamped on as soon as possible. Men rarely have this problem with their mates, but girls have a tendency to become possessive and jealous as soon as someone cute borrows their Latin text-book.

Nobody finds it easy finding a boyfriend or a girlfriend. Funnily enough, the better-looking you are, the harder it often is – because members of the opposite sex are always intimidated. Like all of us, members of the opposite sex are wracked with self-doubt and can't believe that anyone that good-looking would so much as fart in their anorak.

If you have a wide range of friends (obviously, not all of them are going to be close friends), you not only have the added bonus of having people to go out with, ring up, gossip with, and just generally hang out with but they also have lots of brothers and sisters and other friends. By having ordinary friends, you extend your chances of meeting someone you're actually attracted to and *vice versa*. As I have already said, you are unlikely to meet a candidate for passion sitting at home squeezing your zits.

2 *The dawn of time*

In the dawn of time, so the theories go, women – because they could only get pregnant every nine months – were inevitably attracted to the man who was the strongest hunter and would provide for them. Men, on the other hand, wanted to get as many women pregnant as possible, in order to keep the species ticking over nicely. Translated into more modern terms, this forms a very basic theory for the secrets of attraction and the differences between men and women. Up until the last twenty years, nobody ever really questioned this way of thinking. Women were attracted to very powerful men and men wanted to shag everything that moved.

What is courtship?

You may just think you're getting ready to go out but, in fact, it is very likely you will end up reproducing the exact courtship rituals which human beings have always indulged in. These rituals are basically – any time, any place, but not with any one. People are much more careful about choosing their partners than they are about time or place. They pick and they choose and the selection process is called courtship. Most of us think of it as attracting a mate to say 'Yes' to, but it is also saying 'No'. Courtship attracts but equally it repels those you aren't interested in.

You may think your shocking pink lipgloss or your new Doc Martens are hitting high points of allure, when it's probably just down to the way you're standing. The courtship of men and women is different to that of monkeys and apes because

men and women can make love when or where they choose. Every other animal has a season for mating. However, our courtship is the same as that of a peacock with a peahen or a corgi with a corgiette, i.e. it occurs between members of the same species. Courtship is all to do with the messages our bodies send out to each other – different physical signals and displays that we're often not even aware of.

Before we make love, the messages we exchange are mainly about proximity. Men and women indicate their interest to one another in terms of how close they will allow someone to approach them. This kind of courtship is leading up to some kind of sexual contact which makes physical closeness imperative – unless you are a grunion, which is a sardine which can mate without touching, and therefore doesn't have the need to go to wine bars.

Before you even speak to each other the early stages of courtship have already begun. Before a party, people adorn their bodies with visual gender signs – there's perfume, make-up, soft clothes. Even after you've got to know each other a little, the process relies on touch, smell and sight – all of which may, unknown to you, communicate the mood more blatantly than saying 'Let's snog.' All the earlier preparation, together with facial expressions, body movements and postures, are known as non-verbal communication, which anyone who has gone on holiday to the Greek Islands knows all about. The body language of love is universal.

Most of our facial expressions and body movements come from two more primitive areas in the brain, the mammalian limbic system and the archaic reptilian core, and this means that sex and thought tend to be two different ball games. Which is why we court impulsively and then spend months analysing what happened.

Some of the more obvious come-hither signals which you can look out for are simple things like, when dancing, couples rock together. Then there's the coy look, which combines liking (signalled by direct eye contact) with submissiveness, signalled by the angled, lowered head. The coy look says 'I like you and I won't resist if you manage to pluck up the courage to come over and speak to me.' It says all that without you even moving your lips! Timidity is often a theme in courtship because it encourages partners to draw close without the fear of a big rejection, which is what we're all basically terrified of.

The transition from stranger to boyfriend or girlfriend goes through five different phases: Attention, Recognition, Speech, Touch and Lovemaking. Most people get the bum's rush before the touch phase.

Phase One **Attention**: The attention phase can be reduced to three messages: 'Here I am,' 'I am a boy/girl' and 'I won't tell you to bugger off.' Men cough, boast, talk rather loudly, tell jokes, swear and stand up as straight as possible, pushing their chests out. Girls wear high heels that alter the stance of their body, dresses that cling to their bodies, and perfumes which scent the air around them – their space, in fact. However, girls have also been known to cough, boast and talk rather loudly.

Phase Two **Recognition**: We've all experienced this; it's that lingering moment when you catch someone's eye across a crowded room. Without even speaking, one instinctively knows who is attracted to you at a party.

Phase Three **Speech**: This is the most difficult bit of all. Most people fuck up the minute they open their mouths. Almost automatically, a person can lose their cool the minute they speak, simply because conversation reveals hitherto concealed characteristics about that person. The strain of conversation is the first thing to put your newly-discovered physical closeness to a test. What sometimes may look like a friendly and flirtatious conversation can, in close analysis, be proved to be something entirely different. Sometimes, something is wrong: bodies may not fully face each other, shoulders don't turn towards each other, one person may have their arms crossed. If a girl fancies a bloke, she will toss her head, lick her lips, stick her chest out, and play with her hair. So, if she reacted by backing off whenever he leaned in too close, despite her apparent friendliness, if he had read the signals correctly, he would have realised he didn't stand a chance.

Phase Four **Touching**: Couples who have made it through all the other stages are probably quite exhausted at this point. And now their relationship is ready to make a huge leap towards intimacy. Touch is our most ancient sense. It came before hearing, sight and smell by several million years. It's also the one sense we can't do without. Young babies who aren't frequently cuddled and caressed can die from the neglect and lack of love even if they're well fed and kept warm. As we get closer we need more assurance that everything is going smoothly. We need reassurance that our partner still likes us, and some security. And at this stage, we need more than just verbal assurances to be convinced. So couples rub, embrace, tickle, wrestle, lick, bite and kiss each other. That's before they even think about making love. Because of all this, as parents constantly remind us, Phase Five could sneak up before you even notice it.

Phase Five **Making Love**: Very few courtships actually make it this far. After making love, couples tend to find their own space to be in and put a distance between each other. They sleep, they smoke cigarettes, they play Trivial Pursuits – and you will notice too, that from the lovemaking stage onwards, couples tend not to court each other quite so much. It's because once you've reached Phase Five you're no longer negotiating and reassuring, and hopefully you are feeling secure.

You can pick out couples easily by the way they take their closeness to each other for granted. But the special intimacy of lovemaking can have certain unanticipated effects; it will entirely change your attitude to one another. And after exchanging all these signals and forging a bond, it is sometimes not easily broken. This is something which girls tend to feel more strongly than boys and why girls can get very emotional after making love. So boys, a good idea is *not* to roll over and go to sleep immediately afterwards!

Which leads us to . . .

Things that can go wrong
when you first start to make love

A lot of people find that having petted so marvellously, often for years, the first time they make love it can be incredibly painful and totally unlike you had previously imagined. You might be amazed that he has to work so hard, get so sweaty, and that it takes so long. You may wonder where to put your arms, where to put your legs, and why on earth he or she is pulling those faces. It's very difficult to see someone that you have previously regarded as quite normal suddenly heaving all over you.

Often, the person that a girl has built up into a romantic hero does something not so romantic like leaving his socks on – and completely destroys his allure. You may be worried that your body is somehow inadequate, but it might help you to know that your tummy rolls are probably the last thing on his mind. Instead, you should do what he is doing and that is concentrating on the pleasure of the experience. Some women also worry initially, when they are maybe not getting orgasms, whether or not they should fake them. Lots of women do occasionally fake orgasms (and for some it becomes a problem, because the more they do it the less able they are to broach the subject and explain what would enable them to enjoy sex more). Even worse, their boyfriend thinks everything is going brilliantly and sees no reason, naturally, to change anything he's doing. Then, if you at some point decide to tell him the truth, he will feel totally betrayed and inadequate and you will have set yourselves back a long way.

Here are some of the commonest things that both sexes complain of:

1 Inability to relax: When people are under stress at home or at work, they usually react in one of two ways, and either way affects their sex lives. If stress is unhappy, men and women often withdraw from everyone, and when stress is of a happy kind, such as a new job or a new flat, people often throw themselves so much into their new situation that others feel left out. When these things happen, as they do in nearly every relationship at some time, both partners must be willing to try and relax and do things together, such as walking in the park, which is a perfect opportunity for talking, picnics, etc. All of these things have the added benefit of being both relaxing and intimate, in that they provide the perfect opportunity to share any problems and share any triumphs.

2 Too little foreplay: Timing is also involved here. You can't make love happily knowing that your parents are due home in ten minutes, or knowing that if you stay out very late, you are going to be late for your work in the morning. It is also a good idea to do it whenever you have the most time so that you can experiment.

3 Too little tenderness: No-one likes to feel that they have just been used and then dropped. Tenderness can be anything from a little note to a pat on the back or a peck on the cheek. While women are usually the ones who complain of a lack of affection, men need it too. Almost everyone needs reassurance that they are still loved. And sex alone is not enough.

Girls! How to be more attractive

Girls have an advantage here. There are all sorts of ways of camouflaging the bits of you that you don't like. The first thing to learn if you are going to be happy with your boyfriend, is to be happy with yourself. I am not expecting you to skip around the house singing 'Hoorah! Hoorah! I've got cellulite!' but, corny as it may seem, everyone does have good bits and it is those that you should concentrate on, rather than loathing yourself for something you may not be able to alter.

One of the first things that girls imagine they should do in order to be more attractive is to weigh about three stone. They put themselves on punishing and depressing diets that have absolutely nothing to do with nutrition. After this starts, they get tired, they get moody, and they can't sleep. A ludicrous diet is the first step to being really rotten to yourself. It's hard for other people to love you unless you love yourself a little bit. It's a bit like when you walk into the room saying 'My God, but I'm a horrible ankle-snapper,' and everyone feels forced to agree with you.

At the end of a happy morning discussing the size of Victoria Principal's bosoms with Joan Rivers, we all decided that one of the most important beauty tips to remember was camouflage. Why on earth would any sensible girl want to starve herself, do exercises, and make herself miserable, when instead a little bit of common sense can go a long way? It has been said over and over and over again that you don't *have* to eat the puddings at school dinners, there is no law forcing you to eat three Bounty bars on the way home, and vegetables, fruit and fish never put a pound on anybody unless they are covered in batter, deep fried and used in conjunction with a diet consisting entirely of Hula Hoops.

Most girls don't have the time to get up at five in the morning to go to a gym. And a lot of girls would be very bored anyway. It is a good idea figure-wise to try and get an interest in swimming, even if the only way you can cultivate your interest is to go in a gang. Very few people want to work their body. I have absolutely no desire whatsoever to 'locate my hip', as Jane Fonda puts it. I want to be on the sofa in front of *The Sullivans* with a large box of chocolates, preferably not looking too gross. Because of this preference, I am rather hoping that there will be a return in popularity of the roll-on. Roll-ons – or girdles – are wondrous creations that are constantly sneered at. They will stop you looking like a floral upholstered bratwurst tied up in the middle with a belt and transform you, albeit temporarily, into something more svelte. In the meantime, you should be pounding up and down the local baths solidifying everything. Life is too short to starve yourselves, however many magazines you can blame for making you want to be thin. As Joan Rivers said, if God had wanted girls to do exercise, He would have put diamonds on the floor.

When on a diet, there is absolutely no point in having photographs of gorgeous girls stuck on the front of your fridge door. A lot of fashion magazines say you should put a photo of Christie Brinkley between you and the food. I have tried this. And the net effect is massive depression. You wake up and come downstairs to confront this bronzed goddess on the Zanussi Turbofrost and the automatic reaction is to desperately seek comfort in the nearest box of Ready Brek.

So what you should actually do is have pictures of people who are utterly revolting – somebody you are almost certainly better-looking than. You come down in the morning, what do you think? You feel wonderful. You think 'God, I'm already ahead, I'm doing really well on this diet.' It is instilling a feeling of self-confidence rather than thinking to oneself 'What the hell is the point of this diet, I'm never going to look like her, should I shoot myself or have a massive cooked breakfast?' The obvious answer to this is, of course, the massive cooked breakfast.

It's important to remember also that only one in twenty girls is in any way anatomically predisposed towards having a model girl figure. No diet, no amount of Nautilus, can change your basic body shape. It is also worth knowing that many, many of the world's top models live on a near-starvation diet and are constantly hungry.

Legs you would gladly swap ...

(1) Nothing can beat a pair of trousers. Choose those with deep pleats so that they fall smoothly over fat legs and flatter skinny ones. (2) If your legs are very short, trousers with wide waistbands will elongate you. (3) If you have saddlebags (which are those lumps on your outer thighs that make you look like you're wearing jodhpurs when you're not), don't be tempted to put a pair of jodhpurs over the top. Loose trousers or a skirt are a better bet.

Plump all over ...

(1) Think of simple, fluid shapes. Your clothes should enhance you, rather than strangle you. Hard as it may be to accept, the body-hugging boob tube may not be the ideal garment for you. Knitwear and things like soft jumpers, however, will be perfect because you have something to put inside. And tailored clothes (particularly padded shoulders, which give you better proportions) are great for disguising lumps and bumps. Try to buy clothes one size too big rather than one size too small. If you can resist the temptation to grow into them, by looking looser, they will give the impression that you are thinner than you are. If they are too tight, you'll just look like an overstuffed sofa. (2) One colour dressing, for a large frame, creates an illusion. Don't worry too much about the shade. Dark colours and neutrals are safe, but you can also try pastels and day-glo colours. (3) Avoid belts.

Stand up straight ...

You may not have realised this, but bad posture is perhaps one of the most common causes of a droopy figure. If you don't stand up straight, your stomach and your bum automatically stick out.

Big bosoms ...

Like it or not, a good bra is essential for those with a voluptuous figure. It immediately creates a firmer, higher shape and is much more comfortable. Man-styled shirts and tailored jackets are the most attractive and if you're at all embarrassed about your bounty, try drawing the eye away from the problem area with a floral print skirt, flashy shoes or that other great distractor, a throat-high bodice with a very low-cut back.

Wide hips . . .
(1) Don't wear anything too baggy as this will make your hips look even bigger. (2) Don't wear trousers with turn-ups. (3) With skirts, the ones with less fabric at the hip are better, although you must always avoid anything too tight. The new long, narrow skirts can be flattering. Mid-calf pleated skirts are sure winners too as long as the fabric lies flat across your hips, otherwise it will look like a tyre. (4) Always remember that a long, below-the-hip sweater is a good line and big shirts worn as overblouses can hide a multitude of sins.

Pot belly . . .
This was one of the things that men loved best about Marilyn Monroe. But women are still very conscious of even a little fat tummy. They also refuse to accept that many, many, many boys adore a little tummy. If you must disguise this weeny flaw, below-the-hip jackets with low-slung belts are one of the best tummy concealers. You should also try a full, gathered skirt.

Big bums . . .
(1) Always go for jackets and sweaters, shirts and dresses with shoulder-pads, as these put everything into proportion. A wide belt will make your shoulders look wider as well. Avoid tight trousers at all costs, and make sure your skirts fit smoothly. Never wear tight underwear because one of the least attractive sights in the world is VPL – Visible Pantie Line.

Final fashion advice . . .
There are a number of things that *no woman should ever do*: (1) Wear black tights with white sandals. (2) Not shave the hairs on your legs and then wear American tan tights over

them so that the hairs stick through. (3) Wear anything satin with slogans written on it, such as 'Rich Bitch' – you would be surprised at how many otherwise sensible people succumb to such temptation. (4) No-one with a rear end bigger than a six-year-old child's should wear a tracksuit. Nor should they ever, ever – unless they resemble Daley Thompson (to whom I would pay big money to see him so attired) wear a tracksuit with high-heeled gold sandals. (5) Never wear leg-warmers pulled up, especially if wearing stretch jeans and ankle boots. (6) No-one less than five feet seven inches tall should ever wear a pencil-line skirt – they'll look like one of those wandering trees in panto.

The most important beauty tip of all is to be honest with your mirror. You are your own most critical judge and quite right too. There's no point in convincing yourself that you look alluring when you're wearing a pink velour tracksuit with 'Hot to Trot' on the back and that knicker line is showing.

What makes a man sexy?

What makes a man sexy? There is, of course, one immediate answer to that question. An answer that seems automatically to spring to mind, but not to print! As ever, in my attempts to become Chelsea's answer to Woodward and Bernstein, I am going to aspire to higher planes of thought than that.

It was unfortunate that the first person I questioned was my air-hostess friend, Patti, who immediately launched into a graphic account of what the seat-belt check is all about. 'Well, it's actually a crotch check, isn't it? To see who's got the best filled trousers,' she informed me before falling off her chair in hysterical giggles. No wonder the men I know get sweaty palms on take-off; they're worried that they won't be allowed a seat-belt if their crotch doesn't come up to British Airways standard size.

My research went from bad to worse. Everyone I spoke to

seemed to think I was compiling a list on how to pick [...]
not what made a man sexy. My friends fantasised a[...]
cross between Albert Einstein and Abraham Lincoln. A[...]
he had eyes that 'spoke to me across the lettuces in[...]
greengrocers,' and a nice smile, he was almost worth missing
two episodes of *The Professionals* for. 'I want a man who
cannot tell a lie,' said one friend, completely straight-faced. I
can't imagine anything worse. Will he wake up in the morning
and romantically murmur to you 'Yuk, you look like death
warmed up, darling'? *I* want a man who can lie with finesse
and style. I then turned to men for assistance; perhaps they
could shed some light. The first rippled his chest at me
through a strategically ripped t-shirt – which meant I immediately forgot what the question was. 'Looks have nothing
to do with it,' he said, 'it's all a matter of self-esteem.' Which
seemed sensible. The second gentleman had been having
trouble with his piles prior to my interrogation so he merely
gazed wearily about him and muttered 'I suppose a tight bum
would be nice . . .'

In the end, I decided that the attributes I felt would make a
man a veritable cocktail of sexual allure were personal to me.
My list doesn't contain the words 'noble', 'kind' or 'consider-
ate' because the man of my dreams is a terrible cad given to
flinging women clad in satin negligées across hotel suites and
pelting them with silver sugared almonds.

I find men who have success, power and/or fame sexy.
However else can one explain the appeal of politicians like
Henry Kissinger? One would be hard pushed to regard
Henry as a natural successor to Errol Flynn, but I'll bet their
address books, let alone anything else, are the same size. His
appeal can't be in his line of chat; who wants to be wooed over
oysters and watercress to the latest hot poop on peace
settlements? The secret of his appeal and of others like him is
obviously the thought of him in his dinky suit in the White
House with the fate of the world in his briefcase. It's an

appeal that dates back to the Stone Age times when women naturally fell for the strongest man who was guaranteed to bring home the bacon, so to speak. Fame also has a way of endowing those blessed with it, instant charisma. Perhaps one hopes that some of it will rub off in the course of the affair. But, believe me, the mystique of famous men lasts only until the first time you do his laundry . . .

Great seducers always have a good line in chat. According to my sources, as gossip columnists always say, this is where Warren Beatty scores astonishingly well. Reports of his steamy phone calls at five in the morning have reached my perky ears several times. I'm only sad I get it all second-hand. But then again, even if he did ring me, I'd just think it was my mother trying to make me feel better. The Irish have a head start on the rest of mankind in this respect. They are truly excellent on the phone, and are blessed with the ability to make 'Have you put the cat out?' sound like an invitation to re-enact great moments from *The French Lieutenant's Woman*. Paddies tell the most terrific fibs along the lines of 'You are the most beautiful woman in creation,' and 'I could never love anyone else after seeing you in your pyjamas.' Needless to say, I am happy to lap it all up. Accents can have this effect, particularly Northern or East End accents. Public school products with plums in their mouths can sometimes be a real turn-off.

Humour also helps. It would help if he didn't just make you go weak at the knees but made you laugh uproariously as well (i.e. Woody Allen with long legs).

So the obvious answer to this dilemma of what makes a man sexy would be an Irish, lorry-driving Warren Beatty who would saunter up (sexy men always saunter) muttering 'Bejazus, what's new, pussy cat?' According to one person, a man is sexy if he's interested. As far as I can see, this is not true. Most men are interested.In fact, one could say they are generally terrible old trollops.

In order to be this incredibly sexy, enigmatic, walking, talking, living doll, this man does require one thing to stop him feeling like a total part – the confidence of ten men combined. Men with confidence move in a special way – rather as if they're moving the crown jewels from A to B. And the lovely thing about men who think they are delicious beings is that you find yourself agreeing with them. Instead of finding this conceit and confidence irritating, I find it endearing and rather sweet. Contrary to popular belief, the fact that a man may have had amorous encounters with half the population over the age of sixteen does arouse one's curiosity. Turning down these men is meant to give one a great feeling of superiority. Needless to say, with that kind of practice behind him, accepting his offer would lead to an even better feeling.

When I was at school I shared a house with twenty-one other girls. We were all regularly visited by a young man who played in the Oxford rugby team and generally cut rather a dash around town. By the end of the first year, such were the tables of his activities that, like lambs to the slaughter or sheep to the dip, everyone fell for him. He took this for granted, as though it was totally natural for a whole house to be besotted with him. By the end of our second year he'd slept with twenty out of twenty-two girls. This is the success born of confidence.

Men who are totally uninterested and unavailable are also quite fab. Unrequited love does come as something of a shock to those of us who had previously thought of ourselves as a heady mixture of Helen of Troy and Dolores del Rio. Having nil effect on the flavour of the month can be an astonishing feeling. It's also a great excuse for lying flat on your bed, ridden with angst and letting the dust pile up around you. If you are the sort of woman who finds a man sexy only if he's foul to you, then take up a hobby. You can then re-do the Bayeux Tapestry while he comes round to your way of thinking. Then you can go off him and drop him like a hot cake.

And last but by no means least, a sexy man must possess great and astounding good looks. Only a total wally would say that looks don't matter. I still firmly believe that no man under six feet tall has any place in the general scheme of things and nothing can shake me from this belief. Yet every dogmatic thought I've ever had about what exactly constitutes good looks has been severely pummelled in its time. This week, he should have big muscles and behave like Howard Keel in *Seven Brides for Seven Brothers*. However, in ten minutes, a wasted youth with thighs like cocktail sticks may become my perfect dreamboat.

Inevitably, what makes a man sexy changes every time you see a sexy man. By its very nature, what makes these people sexy is really indefinable. It is an aura, a glance, a touch, a fleeting moment as he moves towards the hardware counter. So what may be Howard Keel today may be Russ Tamblyn tomorrow. Back to the cold shower.

BOYS! HOW TO BE MORE ATTRACTIVE

All boys can become more attractive by simply following a few guidelines. I find that being six foot two, very dark and handsome with a devilish sneer to the lips helps enormously. But one doesn't want to spend the whole of one's adolescence waiting to 'shoot up' despite the fact that everyone's mother tells them constantly they're about to grow a foot in a week. My own dear mother, when thwarted in this theory, claims I never 'shot up' because I spent too much time in nightclubs.

However, while you wait to become tall, dark and exquisitely chiselled, here are some pointers: (1) Washing oneself occasionally increases one's allure in leaps and bounds. (2) Food stains, nylon tracksuits, any form of t-shirt with slogans on it like 'I'm with Stupid' are all deeply nonsexy. (3) Girls will look at you with less pity and condescension if you don't allow yourself to get fat. Excess flab is quite hideous at any age, but it's particularly hideous if part of your life may have to be spent in athletic pursuits (i.e. shorts or trunks) or if you ever plan to take your clothes off.

One of the other problems of excess weight is, of course, clothes. Demis Roussos style marquees are not largely featured in men's fashion spreads and for men who face such hideous problems as exploding buttons tautly stretched across undulating stomachs, my only advice would be to lose it rather than even endeavour to disguise it. (4) If it is impossible to shift your fat, spots, perpetually lank hair or a combination of all the above crises, chat, flattery and humour do have great effect upon even the most surly and image-conscious woman. It is important to remember that virtually no woman will ever argue with you if you tell her she's fabulous looking. One of my greatest friends has a body created entirely by the intake of literally gallons of Newcastle Brown Ale and he is utterly irresistible to women because of his glittering anecdotes and winsome charm. He is also, interestingly enough, very unselfconscious about his volume. At the recent wedding of some friends, all the pictures included his knob on the bride's frock. If one is struggling against one's appearance it is also a good plan *never* to mention it, i.e. don't start chatting up a girl with 'Yes, well, I am hideously unattractive.' It's not likely to make her hot and feverish. And remember, sumo wrestlers are not notorious womanisers!

Questions and answers

Q There's a boy at school who's really horrible to me. My mother says he probably likes me. What on earth does she mean?

A   Your mother is right. Strange as it may seem, young men, when they are first getting used to the idea of going out with girls, often aren't quite sure how to communicate this interest. As far as they can see the easiest way to attract anyone's attention is to thump them – and this they do with impunity. However, having grabbed your attention so subtly, he's then probably rather worried that his friends will notice his interest and tease him to death. So he follows up the thump with a few insults, such as 'Hello porky' and 'How'd the homework go, cross-eyes?' If you like this boy back, then it is a good idea to either start teasing him in return, or try and catch him when he's on his own and offer him half your Twix. It is still true that the way to a man's heart is through his stomach.

Q   I am a very fat boy. But my mother always wants me to eat everything on my plate and refuses to let me go on a diet. What can I do?

A   Mothers, by their very nature, have a tendency to imagine that a fat boy is a healthy boy. And, hard as it may be to imagine, one of the great pleasures of motherhood is watching your offspring clear his plate. However, I am sure your mother is sensitive to the fact that you may be being teased about being overweight. If you get pocket money, it would be a good idea to invest in a little book about nutrition. Not diets, the very word will send your mother into a frenzy of worry. However, if you word it so that you sound as if you're interested in becoming more healthy (and perhaps couple this with extra football practice and a bit of running) she will no doubt fall for this ploy. Do not let your mother think that you are merely starving yourself in order to pull girls. All that will happen then is that you will get dumplings three times a day. Of course, the other problem might be school dinners. If your mother has to make you a packed lunch, why don't you suggest a small salad with chicken or a wholemeal sandwich. If you find you need something else, take an apple or an orange. You can always sell the bar of Dairy Milk that she won't be able to resist putting in. In the evening, you could suggest that she makes something like stir-fried chicken and vegetables or a vegetable soup. You may find that the whole family quite fancies your new athletic diet. Let her think that you merely wish to become athletic. Every mother yearns to have Carl Lewis come home in the evening when a Ronnie Corbett look-a-like left in the morning.

Q My elder sister has entirely stopped eating. My parents still don't know. At meals she has little portions but I know she makes herself sick. She also lies to my mother and says that she's eaten earlier or with friends. I'm very worried about her, her hair is falling out and I think her periods have stopped.

A Some girls have such a distorted body image that no matter how thin they get, when they look in the mirror they see a fat girl staring back. So they stop eating or, still more damaging, make themselves sick in private afterwards whenever they are forced to eat. This is called anorexia, and is a serious condition needing medical aid. You should talk to your mother about your sister because she does need help. Anorexia can be fatal; girls become so thin that they can die from starvation. It is quite a common problem in our society and your sister is not alone. Magazines and soap operas show us images of girls who appear to have everything – and they are invariably thin. So some girls think that if they starve themselves to slimness, everything will be within their grasp too. In fact, they get cranky, sick and totally obsessed with their bodies

33

to the exclusion of almost everything else. If you tell your mother, she will be able to talk to your family doctor. If he does not feel equipped to help your sister, he may refer her to another doctor who will help, not by force-feeding, but by helping her see her body as it really is. Your sister, because of her distorted body image, is not going to think that she needs help, so you must be as supportive of her as you can when she is being treated. When she is back to a normal size and able to see how appallingly thin she used to be, she will understand why you had to turn to help on her behalf.

Q When I am going out at the weekend, I never know what to wear. I don't have a lot of money. How can I organise my clothes quickly without spending too much?

A There are some basic rules you could follow to help you make the most of what you have: (1) The night before you are going out, try and decide what you'd like to wear. See if it needs washing or ironing. (2) If you're only going out with your girlfriends, say to the cinema, wear something that you can wear again that won't have to be washed or dry cleaned immediately. This will save you time and money. (3) It's always a good idea, if you don't have a lot of money, to try and plan your wardrobe around one or two colours, like black and white. Then you can add splashes of colour such as a bright t-shirt or socks or gloves. It also helps you to avoid having to make everything match. (4) Never put dirty clothes back into the wardrobe, because you'll find that's the one thing you want to wear. (5) Spend your spare evenings getting all your clothes into good condition, sewing on loose buttons, mending hems, etc. (6) Thrift shops and secondhand shops, if you have the time to look round them properly, are absolute treasure troves, for knitwear, summer dresses and party frocks. Nearly every town has a few and they're a must if you're on a tight budget and want to create a bit of style.

3 *How to be cute*

Feeling at home in your body

Feeling at home in your own body makes feeling at ease with
your boyfriend or girlfriend a lot easier. When you're dressed,
you can do a lot of different things to create certain illusions.
You can wear heels to look taller, black to make you slimmer,
or wear clothes that link you with a certain group of people.
But in the bedroom, Cortina or on the beach, your body has
to speak for itself. So it's rather unnerving and can immediately make you feel very vulnerable.

You would've thought that after years of scrutinising your
body you would have known not only exactly what it looked
like from every angle, but also which were your best bits as
well as your bad bits. You'd imagine that you would know if
you had a beautiful smile, glorious blue eyes or shell-like
ears. Unfortunately, although this is logical, it is not true. We
are often our body's worst critic, pinching at invisible flab or
crazed with misery over a funny nose which nobody else has
noticed. This isn't just modesty; it has been proven that
women usually suffer from a very distorted body image. In a
class of fifth-year girls, 75% when asked, honestly ranked
themselves the least attractive girl in the class. And if you
think you get better as you get older, you'd be wrong again.
Almost 70% of older women studied described themselves as
overweight, when in fact only 39% actually were.

Where do all these body hang-ups come from? A lot of
them start when you are still a small child – the body you see
in the mirror reflects your mental image of your body and not

necessarily what it really looks like. This mental snapshot is
created when you started to grow up from being a baby. It is
then you start to see yourself in terms of big/small, fat/thin,
pretty/ugly, clever/stupid. A strong, gorgeous baby that gets
constantly petted and complimented even before it understands what's being said, has a good head start on feeling
good about his or her body. Another contributing factor is
how you are placed within your family. Often, other sisters
and brothers might be considered by everyone to be the
pretty, clever, or sporty one in the family. So you might find
yourself growing up constantly comparing yourself with a
sister that's supposedly much better looking or a brother with
an IQ of 987.

Then there's the attitude of your friends. They might tease
you incessantly about your ears sticking out or the fact that

you're useless in gym. Gym, you will be glad to hear, may no longer be a large part of your life by the time you're eighteen, but you'll probably still be thinking of yourself in a negative way.

All these things can add up and make it very hard for you to truly see yourself as you really are. One of the ways to tell how bad your body image is by asking yourself the following questions: (1) Do you keep off the beach because you don't want anyone to see you in a pair of trunks or a bikini? (2) Do you avoid gym or athletics because you feel your bum's going to hang out of your shorts? (3) Do you ever deliberately not go to parties because you can't seem to get yourself looking right? (4) Do you avoid communal changing rooms because you feel that everyone's looking at you?

If you answer 'yes' to some of the above questions, you have a poor body image. But there is something you can do about that. Ask yourself, could your body really do with losing a little weight, or does it maybe just need to be firmed up a bit? If you find you are depressed about the shape of your body, remember that the mood-uplifting qualities of getting regular exercise are well-documented. It also seems that athletes, because they know their bodies well, are better at assessing the true size and shape of them.

If spots are your problem, ask your local chemist to recommend one of the inexpensive skincare ranges aimed at problem skin. They don't break the bank and combined with watching what you eat – no fried foods, chocolates or fizzy drinks – may help a lot. You should stick to the regime religiously and it will really pay off. It's no good just occasionally cleansing your face if you do tend towards spots; you need to do it twice a day.

Modesty

Cora Pearl was often referred to as the Queen of the Courtesans. She had the whole thing sussed. Not for Cora the dismal road of learning to be a good kisser and a divine conversationalist, or to change her sheets frequently – she just *lay there*! Cora's success came from lying stock still in her bedroom, which was decorated like the Naughty Nineties' answer to Shea Stadium. In front of her sixteen foot high gold bed, draped with red damask and trimmed with the pelts of several small men, there was an extensive seating arrangement for the aristocracy. She then held her morning 'receptions'. Men paid small fortunes to attend these, even straight after a large plate of fried eggs and kidneys at home. Once everyone who had coughed up the dough was seated, a flunkey dressed in green livery would whip away Cora's red satin covering and there she would lie, naked in all her milk white splendour, for five minutes. Then everyone went home again until the next week.

If that had been me, I would have been twitching like I'd just been hung. But then *some people have no shame* . . . and I seem to have everyone else's share. I hasten to add that I have not always been like this. Up to the age of six I was more than happy to sing 'Let Me Entertain You' to the vicar, with a rousing finale which involved showing him my bottom. Even twelve years after that I was OK. But by nineteen I was unwilling to take my slip off for anything. I sympathised greatly with Jeremy Irons when he was teased for attaching his underpants to the sheets with a safety pin in *Brideshead Revisited* during a love scene, and relieved when Brooke Shields stuck her hair to her bosom with Bostik for *The Blue Lagoon*.

I'm doomed to eternity to be the girl gyrating furiously on the beach, getting enough sand up her bum to re-concrete the entire frontage of Centre Point. That's just getting my very one-piece swimsuit on under the protective covering of at least fourteen different towels. I won't go into communal changing rooms at Miss Selfridge. That's not just because of the strain of getting into trousers under a pencil skirt while still wearing a floor-length yashmak, but also because I get a headache trying to work out why so many girls wear their knickers over their tights with the whole ensemble seductively topped off with a greying bra *over* a vest. It's true, I've seen it – all human life is in a communal changing room. However, they're not going to see mine unless I've been in training. When I did go into training at a gym, the most energetic thing I did was getting from the changing room to the rowing machine in my shorts without anyone seeing my thighs, which often resemble something grey and throbbing that you might get for dessert at school.

In the agony columns, women ponder men's weirdness: 'My boyfriend wants me to make love on the floor next to the french windows which lead to the goldfish pond' . . . 'My boyfriend wants me to make love with all the lights on.' *POOH*! I'm waiting for mine to join some exotic religious sect so we can start doing it *through* the duvet, let alone turning the place into some makeshift *son et lumière*.

Then there are the girls that men dream of, uninhibited women who enter wet t-shirt contests and bring their own hosepipe. I've a friend who's a perfect Rubens peach with a large plum in her mouth. She likes to frolic – and I mean frolic – at every opportunity. Hoovering is all the excuse she needs to doff her clothes and skip, Isadora Duncan-style, up and down in front of wafting curtains, trilling to herself. She was horrified recently when, mid-bodge, her lover realised that her curtainless boudoir was overlooked by approximately four hundred other dwellings. He promptly rolled on to the floor and crawled on all fours up the hallway to the loo where he wrapped his groin in a J-cloth which was all that was handy. 'How bourgeois,' she muttered darkly to me.

Accusations such as 'repressed' and 'inhibited' are always

flung at the modest by the frolicsome. The frolicsome try and shame the modest into thinking that not having a rampant desire to expose one's ribs to the populace indicates a hideous working-class upbringing, eating only gruel, sleeping in one's underwear and taking one bath a year, sharing the water with fourteen miners. In fact, a helluva lot of modest people come from public schools where boys take their baths in their trunks and girls get dressed in bed. One man told me to try to 'act a bit more bohemian', which sent me into such a flap that I spent all night sitting on the bedside table worrying what I'd do if I didn't wake up looking like Audrey Hepburn in a black crew neck and ski pants.

One of the other main problems with being obsessed with one's body is that of course you are obsessed with everyone else's as well. I start to act like something out of Raymond Chandler when *Dallas* is on. My eyes narrow to viperish gimlets glaring ferociously into Victoria Principal's narrow back, my respiration increases to heaving point when she turns around, only to be given a breathing space by the appearance of Lucy, who's possibly the only person in the States shorter than me. I'm one of the few women who went to see *Cat People* just to see what Nastassia Kinski looked like tied naked to a bed, and when she did that poster wrapped in a ninety-three foot anaconda *three* different people gave me a copy. I get so insecure about so much that lurks below neck level, that I end up hiding magazines under the sofa if Joan Collins or Selina Scott are in them. I always imagine my boyfriend will spend hours perusing Joan's crevices, look for mine and immediately leave home.

Another problem, of course, is hypochondria. If one has spent most of the morning perched on the side of the bath in order to look at one's thighs in the bathroom cabinet mirror, one is acutely aware of every throb and jiggle. My body throbs and jiggles a great deal, so I constantly think I have terminal illnesses. So aware am I of its every twinge that I only need to suspect a sore throat to take to my bed wrapped in brown paper coated in mustard. A headache and it's a brain tumour. One of the most thrilling moments of the last six months was being told by an earnest intern at casualty that I had house-maid's knee on my toe.

But I remain convinced that excessive modesty and gay abandoned bohemian behaviour probably come from the same unsavoury root: contemplating one's every sinew, muscle and undulation and wondering who we should show it to next . . .

People who do have a bad body image and constantly think of themselves as being fatter and uglier than they really are, tend to go one of two ways: they either compensate or avoid. They compensate by concentrating on another attribute, which is why boys often find that a girl that isn't quite so pretty may be a lot funnier. Or, they avoid the issue and stop going out, dressing in unattractive clothes, and become more and more introverted.

As you obviously want to avoid spending your entire teenage years in your room, you need to bring your problem down to size. If you think you're clumsy, have you thought about taking a dance class? This will help your coordination and you'll meet a few more people, some of whom are bound to be clumsier than you. Often, taking lessons in a sport will have the same effect. Have you thought about tennis, squash or badminton? Inevitably, most sports have a whole social side to them as well.

What to do when you achieve body confidence? *FLAUNT IT!*

Getting your gear off

Once you feel all right in a swimsuit, the next problem is what happens if you have to take all your clothes off. And since this book is about sex, that is likely to happen. If you fear that your

41

body won't pass some kind of test, that he or she won't think it measures up, or that in some way you are not the ideal shape that you see in magazines, it can really affect your enjoyment of sex. You'll find you won't want to try certain positions in case your stomach looks like Michelin Man. Or, just as bad, you may be trying them and not enjoying them because of the strain of holding your stomach in. Not having a lot of sexual confidence is not a female prerogative; a lot of boys feel they won't be able to compete in the sexual athletics. Men worry about standing up to the stud image.

People shouldn't like you just because of what your body looks like. Having long legs or a slim waist or perfect teeth and skin isn't a passport to happiness, or a guarantee that someone will love you forever. In fact, although obviously all these things do help attract people initially, mere looks are a fairly transitory part of a relationship. After a few meetings, few men or women are wanting to just gawp at their partner. They have got to the stage of getting to know each other, doing things together and laughing with each other. And he's not going to leave you just because you forget to shave your legs. But initially, half the battle is knowing your body and liking it. A lot of people don't know their bodies very well; they don't know what feels nice and sometimes they are not even sure if everything's quite normal. It's a good idea to examine every bit of yourself to see what feels like what and, as much as possible, try and stop yourself thinking in terms of ugly or attractive. You should try to think in terms of sensation and texture. Not that this is easy if you are faced with a huge wodge of thigh.

Research has proved that women who are least satisfied with their sex lives are also least satisfied with their genitals. These women were very concerned about the way they might smell, taste, feel or even look to their partners. These fears prevented a lot of women from ever really looking at or feeling the bits of their bodies that were worrying them so much. If you can't put a name to everything that you see when you do investigate, get a medical encyclopaedia out of the library. The better you know your body, the better you will automatically feel about it. Knowing a lot about something takes away a lot of the fear.

No-one would go out wearing a dress or a pair of trousers that they had never laid eyes on before. So it's a good idea to regard your body in the same light.

Knowing what you like and don't like

This takes a little experimenting and involves a certain amount of trial and error. By this I hasten to add that I don't mean trying hundreds of different people. Far better to have one person you feel secure with and know that when you wake up in the morning, the relationship will still exist. From this firm basis you will find that you feel confident enough to experiment more. It's also difficult to learn to experiment without hurting your partner's feelings. She or he might think that they were doing it all wrong and feel dreadful – she'd be convinced that she should be like Rosanna Arquette in *Desperately Seeking Susan* – he'd be convinced he should be like Don Johnson in *Miami Vice*! Even if the criticism you want to make is entirely justified (i.e. you really *don't* like him putting his toe in your ear) sex is one of those subjects, like religion and politics, that can get people very upset. What you may feel is a perfectly reasonable comment, may come as a large bucket of cold water flung over the steaming bed of romance.

So how do you broach things? Anything that you want to say that could be taken as a criticism should be worded very carefully. Never say 'You are doing xxxx wrong' but instead, try 'I would like it even more if you didn't put your toe in my ear.' It's also a good idea not to make these sort of comments in bed but maybe the next day, over a bacon sandwich or something entirely unsexual. Picking the wrong moment can

43

make things much harder to repair. For both men and women, sex is such a vulnerable area that a little tact goes a very long way. The better you know someone, the more you trust them. And the easier it is to be the real you, both emotionally and physically.

So when you first meet someone, take things step by step. There is absolutely no hurry to get to know each other faster than you feel comfortable with.

Playing hard to get

I am a great believer in playing hard to get – the potency of the initially unobtainable . . . the thrill of prolonging the first touch of skin on skin . . . the tremble of anticipation spread out as long as possible without you actually eating photos of him in bed. Too many women today, in their efforts not to appear turgid, enjoy the sins of the flesh, and captivate their quarry, but miss out on the old-fashioned charms of the chase. My friends all seem incapable of keeping their hands on their ha'pennies for longer than three hours and their idea of being aloof is making him wait till after the pudding. One friend recently launched herself like Sputnik at the man who came to fix her Potterton simply because she 'liked the way his spanner was sticking out.'

Women are thus depriving themselves of moments straight out of *cinéma noir* when car windows steam up, walls stream with condensation And begonias do remarkably well. I wouldn't recommend anyone to embark on the romance of the decade after two hours of watching Pearl & Dean commercials, followed by half a Big Mac eaten in a light drizzle off Lower Regent Street. Far better to endure hours of steaming longing, the building up of a deafening crescendo, when one's entire body turns red like a freshly scalded prawn ball.

Sex today is in danger of becoming something instant,

lukewarm and resembling a tomato-covered, wormlike Pot Noodle. Girls relive scenes from *Dallas* with men whose Coke bottle they wouldn't dream of drinking out of. A return to the old-fashioned values seems in order. Teenagers have the right idea. They inevitably fancy the only boy at the disco/youth club/Bar-B-Q who wouldn't fancy them even if they had four rolls of Andrex stuffed down the front of their Wonderbra. This is why all teenagers, according to problem pages, imagine that their entire lovelife is going to be spent swooning over disinterested men. When one is grown-up, of course, this changes, but who doesn't remember the angst-ridden pleasure of hankering for a few weeks (before the searing culmination near the bike shed) with someone invariably called Nigel? Doris Day had the right idea when she kept James Garner at bay for literally movie after movie while she changed her ski pants every fourteen minutes. Meanwhile, Jim was stuck in the adjoining bathroom in his PJ bottoms looking hopeful.

The whole thing of playing hard to get is tactics. It's a matter of perfecting the art of delaying action, of appearing aloof, disinterested and intriguing without appearing to have quaffed half a bottle of Ribena and a handful of Anadin before you came out. It is not only a matter of having a seductive mystique, it also demands great physical control. A woman who's hoping to drive him insane with desire by appearing vaguely remote, mustn't cackle hilariously at all his jokes or spill her food or fall over anything. Falling over is the absolute kiss of death, because once he's realised you really are a nit like him, that's it. A woman must imagine she's evoking the passion of every play ever set in the Deep South, she must pulsate like Sue Ellen does with Dusty and she has to remember the chess game in the *Thomas Crown Affair*.

You only have to look at who's sexy to see the lure of the unobtainable. SEXIEST THING EVER was Paul Newman as Gubba in *Cat On a Hot Tin Roof* because he *never* wanted to do it, even when faced with Elizabeth Taylor in a slip. Brooke Shields is sexy even though she doesn't do it. I mean, do you imagine that she let John Travolta kiss her *with his mouth open* on the first date! No way – Brooke knows that heavy petting leads to Worse Things. Dr Kildare was sexy, as are many gynaecologists because all you get is suppositories (and that's if you're lucky). Michael Jackson is sexy – maybe he does talk to shop dummies, has had his balls bitten off by an Australian sheep dipper and cry a lot (if gossip is to be believed) but he is still an icon of crumpet because Michael Jackson believes that sex before marriage is a sin. This has to be the sexiest statement ever and leads most of the planet to live in hope that maybe one day he'll marry and then make love.

Catholics are also sexy because they feel guilty about everything and have to cross themselves even if they take their vest off too fast. *The Thorn Birds* was sexy to a lot of people because 'she' was in love with a Catholic priest who was also Dr Kildare – which killed two birds with one stone, so to speak. And Montgomery Clift's still sexy and he's dead, and you can't get much more unavailable than that.

One friend held an Arab suitor at arm's length for a record three days, only to be plied with gifts (a bonus, I suppose). I received a breathless phone call informing me he'd presented her rather esoterically with 'two Louis Vuitton suitcases and a Gucci bottle opener'. I now think he probably thought that giving her a bleeding bottle opener was wildly symbolic. However, in her efforts to keep Lebanon's answer to Warren Beatty at bay, she didn't go to his house. And it's amazing how revealing that can ultimately be, as she discovered when he opened his beaten silver front door to her with an abandoned flourish ... What awaited her, on the evening eventually chosen as the Night of the Seven Veils, made her reel back, flinging her Gucci bottle opener at his red tooled leather stereo cabinet. All the glass tables rested on the stuffed heads of various tusked animals. Above a circular bed was a mirror surrounded by red lights and the whole erotic love nest was finished off with a wolfskin duvet cover. My friend, a woman of *immense* aesthetic sensibilities, left pronto, ever grateful that she hadn't surrendered her honour on the first night in the back of his metallic blue Roller.

But one of the main things to avoid in the minefield of playing hard to get is taking a friend along as support. You'll probably lose the friend. I was asked by my unbelievably beautiful schoolfriend to accompany her and some mad Russian prince to a fish dinner. Not realising that she was wildly keen, I wore an appalling tracksuit and set off. When I arrived, she was wearing her entire family jewels and had POWDERED HER BOSOMS and left most of them out in the cold. The Russian prince, whose name was Vlad, was straining over his cod. At the sight of me, though, he resorted to his only tactic – COMPARISON! 'Aaaaahhh, Debbie,' he said to her over the candles as I picked grubs off my jersey. 'You have a neck like a swan, and she, the poor girl, has one like a turkey.' By the end of the dinner, I was ready to fling myself in with the lobsters but instead I just stomped off into the night minus my friend with the neck like a swan.

But finally, remember the essence of being on a pedestal for a couple of months is timing. If you are hoping to emulate the icy glory of Grace Kelly, just spare a thought for what happened to Warren Beatty and Natalie Wood in *Splendour in the Grass*. She left it a couple of days too late and topped herself due to an excess of hormones, and he, Mr What's New Pussycat? himself, went mad . . .

Questions and answers

Q I always think that I would do better in my exams, get on better with my parents and get the boyfriend I want if only I didn't have such a big nose.

A Often, hating a certain part of your body is really just a way of disguising the things you are really afraid of. It is easy to blame a big nose for bad CSE results or family rows. Research has shown that people who have real physical handicaps and actually do have good reason for blaming their bodies for certain aspects of their lives are often able to accept their bodies and feel happier about themselves than those who spend their time longing for a perfect nose.

People who have completely normal and healthy bodies and don't have to deal with a real physical handicap every day of their lives frequently concentrate on some imagined flaw as an excuse for not really trying. It's easier to say 'I don't have a boyfriend because of my nose' than admitting that perhaps you don't have a boyfriend because you're a frightful old misery that nobody wants to go out with. Other people may use their imaginary flaw as a way of avoiding what many teenagers see as a very competitive social situation that they are afraid of not measuring up to. While it's true that if you keep up the facade of not caring and not trying you'll never lose, if you don't play the game you can't win – and won't have any of the fun along the way.

If you are lucky enough to have a brutally honest friend, it might be a good idea to ask her honest opinion of your nose. Is it really so awful or have you just literally blown it out of proportion because you are depressed or unhappy about other things in your life? If you actually do look like Jimmy Durante or Cyrano de Bergerac's uglier younger cousin, it is possible to have plastic surgery on the NHS if your doctor feels that it is causing you psychological damage. It is also possible that if in some way your nose is actually damaged i.e. you may at one time have broken it or had sinus troubles, that is another excuse for NHS treatment. But be wary, very often, young people who have plastic surgery – say, on their nose – then start blaming some other part of their bodies for what's the matter with their lives. It's an expensive and painful way of dealing with problems which could be solved more efficiently with a bit of calm thinking and talking to someone sympathetic. You will probably find that they are just as dissatisfied with some part of themselves, but they have learned to live with it – even enjoy its uniqueness.

Q I hate having my picture taken. And I soon have to have a portrait taken for my passport. What should I do?

A Some people can't resist photographs because for them, they're just a record of a happy day. For others, they are a record of all the various things that they think are hideously wrong with them. For them, a photograph is a good reason to retire on to the sofa staring at various lumps and bumps. What I would suggest is that if you do want to go abroad, you will have to steel yourself and have the picture taken. The only way you can make this slightly better is if you spend the morning before the picture is taken tarting yourself up. That way, there will be as few faults on show as possible. And you are more likely to feel happy about flashing your passport at border guards. It is a well-known fact that everyone looks like a mass murderer in their passport pictures anyway.

4 *Parents*

Parents and their problems

There is no greater passion-killer than parents. Almost everyone has a tale to tell about their parents either entirely putting the kybosh on what promised to become the greatest romance of the century, or about the time they came walking in on the romance of the century and reduced you to a person with all the sensual allure of Andy Pandy. Parents have a way of always treating you as though you're three years old, regardless of who's there watching.

Most people are able to remember their first kiss with something approaching a nostalgic rosy glow. I am not one of them. My first kiss romantically occurred on a cliff-top when I was twelve, and was interrupted by my mother running along the path towards us, screaming like a banshee, smacking us both on the back of the head and knocking us into the sea. As I emerged from the water I was dragged along the beach by my swimming costume strap in full view of everyone and locked in the car, while my mother flounced off to sit on the beach for the rest of the day. So I too have experience of parents being a little over-protective.

In my mother's case, as with many other mums, one of the reasons that they feel they want to protect you from what might happen, is because they vividly remember how they behaved when they were your age. Fathers may not strike you as tumultuous cauldrons of passion as you watch them shovelling in the beans on toast, eyes glued to Match of the Day. But in fact, they may have waved their Sword of Union quite indiscriminately throughout their teenage years. So, when you bring round your new boyfriend, they do a Uri Geller, they know exactly what he's thinking, and would willingly write it on a piece of paper inside a sealed envelope without a Biro! They know exactly what they did with their girlfriends – and they remember that their parents (your grandparents, if you're beginning to get confused) weren't too happy about it either, so there's no way that some smooth Romeo's going to behave like that with their little girl (no matter how much their little girl may be up for it).

Mothers, on the other hand, have a two-way problem. The first bit is that their teenage years were probably left behind with black and white telly, wirelesses and Victor Sylvester, and they may feel slightly jealous of a daughter's youth and freedom. Then sometimes, mums (and dads) feel that they are just around to provide meals, new shoes and a taxi service on a daily basis, and they miss all the cuddles and kisses they got when you were little – and are very jealous to see you now doling out those kisses and cuddles to someone else. And with sons, mums might feel the ultimate double standard – a sort of pride that their boy's doing so well with so many girls, and at the same time feeling absolutely positive that no girl will ever be good enough for their little boy.

Which brings us to my next point. One of the great problems of having parents, is that, rather like ninety-year-olds who say they feel exactly the same as they did when they were twenty-five, when you are twenty-five (or even fifty) your mother and father will still be referring to you privately as 'the baby'. Maybe it's because, hard as it may be for you to imagine, having you was probably a great moment in their love story and they remember very clearly waiting-for-you, you-arriving and you-as-a-small-child. And how you were The Most Beautiful Baby That Ever Existed In The History Of The Whole World, and they knew that – purely objectively of course – because everyone told them it was true. So when you come into the kitchen slightly drunk, covered in spots and car grease, and your mother screams, it's because she still expects you to look like the little angel you once were.

A lot of the problems that parents have are because it's almost impossible for many of them to reconcile the fact that the child that once loved them so passionately and was so dependent on them, has drawn away from them (as every child must, if a parent has done their job properly). But you should realise that, by your drawing away, someone they once felt so close to has suddenly become a stranger – someone they have almost nothing in common with. And that confuses and hurts them.

The blame is not entirely to be put at your parents' doorstep. While they may be telling you the right way for you to live your life, it is worth remembering, I have realised in retrospect, that mothers are often right, annoying as this frequently is. My mother used to say that it was all rather like the Grand National – mothers have already run the course and know all the holes you're likely to fall into. Unfortunately, mothers, in their passion to protect you from these plunges, never quite master diplomacy. But back to doorsteps.

You, on the other hand, are likely to be going through that unfortunate period that everyone has, when they think they know everything. And everyone knows how annoying someone is when they think they know it all, especially when they know three-fifths of fuck all. So your mother or father's kindly meant fragments of advice delivered over the kitchen table are likely to be greeted by a surly silence reminiscent of the Allies being interrogated by the Gestapo. You will be thinking 'What do these boring old farts know, and it's none of their business anyway.' But don't forget your father will have been kept up half the night by your mother poking him in the back asking rhetorical questions such as 'Where is he, what is she doing, do you know the phone number of that nightclub and what time do you think we should call the police.'

For single parents, life is even harder because they have nobody to share these worries and responsibilities with and feel they must be both parents at the same time. You will also be extra precious to them.

In all dealings with all kinds of parents, impossible as it will seem when you just want to be a surly git, and you're forced to live with people you can't even believe you're related to, you have to think of your parents rather as if they're suffering from unrequited love. You have to try and be patient and kind and rather noble about the whole thing, no matter how irritated you are. This will have a major effect: namely, there will be fewer rucks, which everyone wants because it's very hard to ruck with somebody that's being nice (i.e. a little brown-nosing goes a long way). The most simple ways of creating a good ambience are: volunteering to do the washing-up and then doing it properly; keeping your room in some semblance of order; not smelling or looking too disgusting; offering to help with the shopping, loathsome as this is; not coming in and plonking yourself down in front of the television every time you walk through the door; and finally – one of the great bugbears of teenage life – doing your own laundry. Anyone who does all these things would actually have to be a saint, but one or two of these things on a regular basis go a long way to a peaceful existence. This might sound ridiculous, but major family arguments often initially start because your parents are festering over some domestic grievance, such as the washing-up or the state of your bedroom. So get in there first and surprise them.

Parents and sex

When speaking to some young modern types about this book, the first thing they all wanted to know was, if they were paying rent, did it mean they could do It in their parents' houses? Which just goes to show – the callous insensitivity of today's youth! Anyone who sits down for five minutes and thinks of both sides of this intriguing problem will realise that, whether you like it or not, and whether or not you are paying your parents something towards your keep (quite right too, once you are earning a wage) this does not give you the right to turn their house into some out-take from *The Fall of the Roman Empire*. No matter how grown-up you are or how mature you and your girlfriend or boyfriend are being, what it comes down to is this – it is their house and they make the rules. And nobody can say who's right or wrong in these situations.

This problem about where to have sex seems to preoccupy many teenagers more than anything else. Most parents will not allow their children to make love under their roof. This is not because they think particularly that it will stop you doing it, it is because they don't want it going on right next to them. For example, imagine how embarrassing they would find it if they could hear you – just as you would find it embarrassing to walk in on your parents, mid-bodge.

Which brings us back to where do you do it. Every parent, the minute they go out of the front door, imagines this is some kind of secret signal for immediate frenzied sexual activity, which is probably the reason they never take holidays or even go out. But there is this opportunity of using one's own home in the absence of one's parents, but always remembering: (1) Not to wreck the place. (2) Not to drink their drink. (3) *Never* use their bed, and (4) That parents have an annoying tendency to change their plans or row on the way to the seaside and may come home after half an hour only to discover you both entwined round the chandelier in the drawing room! and don't forget (5) You may also think that you're safe on the sofa when your parents have gone to bed at ten o'clock, but parents suffer notoriously from Night Wandering.

When desperation takes over, many people end up doing it in cars in lovers' lanes. You may have a bigger brother or sister who you get on with, with a home of their own who might be willing to let you have your own space there. Even if your parents are liberal enough to suggest that you use your own room, you may well feel too embarrassed about it. It is natural to want privacy and not to want your parents nudging and winking every time you go upstairs to your bedroom.

When it comes to sex, parents can often react angrily and become very hurtful, often unintentionally, because they don't realise that even when you're at the peak of not liking your parents very much, very few of us can ever shake off that habit of seeking their approval. So the father who calls his daughter a fat scrubber is not making huge steps towards *détente*. Fathers often get very angry as their daughters grow up because, in some cases, they see very clearly how attractive they are becoming, and then get worried that there is something seriously wrong with them for even noticing. Because they think these feelings are dreadful, they in turn get angry with their daughters. So one minute, a loving father can be taking his daughter out for treats and the next minute, he is screaming and accusing her of all kinds of things that she is almost certainly not up to. All that a girl can do in these situations is to try to remain loyal and be patient. Because slowly, every father gets used to his daughter growing up and adjusts to it.

If you feel that your parents do not understand you (maybe they don't), it is important to try and remember that they aren't alien beings. Everyone finds it impossible to imagine that their parents ever make love, for example, but I can assure you that almost everybody's do. They have hopes and fears and aspirations which they may feel they have not fulfilled or which they still hope to. All of these things, to a tiny extent, should help you to see your parents as ordinary people who simply belong to a different generation. And there are two sides to this coin: while on the one hand, it would be wonderful if everyone had parents with whom they could discuss sex openly and freely, almost no-one would want the sort of parents that some are blessed with, the kind that want to go out grooving with them to the disco and join in all the time or wear trendy clothes that make you shudder with embarrassment. My own dear mother used to pick me up from school wearing a red wig that reached her bottom, alluringly combined with a bright purple catsuit that had a diamond pattern in red around each of the bell-bottomed trouser legs. Seriously!

So in sexual matters, you have two alternatives and you must use your own discretion and your own knowledge of your family. One is to seek help elsewhere – and there are many addresses at the back of this book which will be helpful. (One thing to remember here is that parents have an almost detective-like tendency to discover the truth, and if they find out something that you have not told them the fracas is likely to be a lot worse than if you tell them in advance.) The second, which is only applicable if you have understanding or liberal parents, is to turn to them for advice and, if possible, come to some kind of amicable arrangement whereby the blossoming of your sexuality doesn't interfere too harshly with the continuance of happy relations with your parents.

Parents and staying out late

For parents and teenagers this is often a subject that is as open to violent disagreements as sexual matters. In fact, in many parents' eyes the two are inextricably linked, particularly fathers, who have an odd tendency to imagine that all sex only occurs under the cloak of darkness.

Staying out late is one of those things where you have to prove yourself, i.e. on the first few trips out, when you have been told to get in by a certain time, you must not be one minute late. It's also a good idea to smarm up by doing things like leaving the phone number of where you'll be, or if there isn't a phone, the address you're going to be at. This is so your father has some evidence to show your mother when she gets worried at about twenty past eight. After the first few trips into the dead of night, your parents will feel slightly less panicky and you will be able to start negotiating to stay out later, especially if there is something special that you wish to go to.

One disadvantage of being the eldest child in the family is that you have to have all the initial battles over what time is appropriate to stay out until, whether you're allowed to bring friends home, etc. It can be very frustrating in later years seeing younger brothers and sisters taking for granted all the things that you used to anguish over and not be allowed to do.

Parents' attitudes to boys and girls are almost invariably going to be different. There is more of a tendency to believe that boys can look after themselves and girls need to be taken more care of. So girls may often have to be home earlier than boys, which can seem incredibly unfair. But it is true that there is more danger for young women out late at night than for young men, so try and understand. Reassure your parents that you never walk down dark streets on your own or make your way home all alone. Always have a taxi fare with you even if you have to scrounge it from your mum and dad. Another good idea if you *are* going out until late at night – and this is worth remembering for yourself not just to pacify your parents – is if you can arrange a lift or a taxi home. It *is* a good deal safer. No-one in their right mind should ever, ever take a lift from a stranger and that includes people you meet at parties who may be slightly drunk and chummy – but you don't *really* know them. This is not just to please your parents. If you are old enough to go out, you are also old enough to be sensible about your safety. There is no charm or maturity in being reckless just for a laugh. And there is nothing funny about a driver who has had too much to drink. That's why you should never sneer at your parents' offers of help when they say they'd like to pick you up from wherever you are going, even if it's the small hours of the morning. You can even make this fun and turn it to your advantage if they can be persuaded to drop a few of your friends home too.

One very sensible rule which seems to work and calms parents down enormously, is if you are going to be late or stay over at a friend's house unexpectedly, promise always to ring. This means they don't think you're dead in a ditch somewhere, which is what parents always tend to imagine and why they worry so much.

Finally, one thing that is always worth remembering in your dealings with your parents, no matter how angry or discontented you may feel, is that one day, it is very likely that you too will be a parent. And unimaginable as this is, you will probably find yourselves saying all the things that make you vomit now.

5 *What actually happens*

Anyone worth their D. H. Lawrence may have had moments of confusion about What Actually Happens. Books inevitably have bizarre euphemisms which further cloud the issue . . . 'Swords of union sing their song of love' while white hot flames are fanned' etc. Biological diagrams are no help either, because it's hard to perceive one's body when it's cross-sectioned like kidneys at the butchers with one leg entirely missing. It may all appear miles away from the back of the Gaumont.

So what actually happens is that the man's penis goes hard and he puts it inside the woman's vagina and then he moves it in and out. Now I've said it, now you know everything – and I used the proper words too. *WHAT MORE CAN YOU ASK FOR???* You may well ask. What actually happens is something most teenagers spend their entire waking lives wondering about. What makes it even more confusing is that it gets called so many different things: they made love, they had sex, they had an affair, they slept together, they went to bed, they shagged, they had intercourse. All of these are expressions for the same thing, which leads us neatly on to the next question. What happens when they're in bed shagging/making love/having an affair, etc? This chapter will describe What Actually Happens. Unfortunately, it may sound like a cross between ludicrously silly and totally unbelievable. It will make you wonder even more about your parents. It might even sound a little dull, but that's because it's impossible to describe many activities without them sounding quite strange. Imagine if I tried to describe a game of cricket, you'd wonder why anyone would do that every Sunday all summer.

To understand how people actually knob, you have to know about male and female sex organs. In schools, there is an odd tendency to immediately describe frogs' sex organs which, as they're green and spongey, confuses the issue somewhat.

How it all starts

GIRLS AND PUBERTY

In adolescence, the shape of the body changes. A girl's legs become longer, her hips become wider, and she generally starts to develop a typically female shape. Her waist becomes narrow, her hips are rounded and her thighs will develop pads of fat. She grows bosoms and hair appears on her body, under her arms and covering her pubic bone. These changes occur because of the body's hormones, which send messages around the body and affect the laying down of new fat. Each month, as the hormones are released into the body, the breasts tend to enlarge; they can sometimes be quite painfully sensitive. Each time the monthly period occurs, a.k.a. menstruating, the curse, being on the rag, the time of the month, etc., the breasts usually lose their tenderness and the cycle starts again.

A girl's ovaries contain all of the eggs that she will shed in her entire life. There are thousands of eggs in each ovary and in puberty the ovaries become active. An egg begins to grow and mature and this happens approximately every twenty-eight days, although many people's cycles may be shorter or longer, or irregular if you are just starting. Irregularity is nothing to worry about. This twenty-eight day cycle is repeated throughout a woman's fertile life until she is in her late forties or early fifties when her periods will stop.

In the first part of the twenty-eight day cycle, the female sex hormone, oestrogen, is produced by the ovary. Around the middle of the cycle, the egg is expelled from the ovary and finds its way into the Fallopian tubes. Little hairs which line the tube carry the egg towards the womb, which takes about three days. If an egg is fertilised by a male sperm, and a baby is conceived, this occurs while the egg is travelling along the Fallopian tube. During the time from the release of the egg a second hormone, called progesterone, is made and this stimulates the lining of the uterus, making it thick for the egg to rest in. The glands in the uterus enlarge and there is an increase of blood supplied to the lining of the womb. If the egg doesn't become fertilised, at about twenty-five days the production of hormones by the ovaries is reduced. Then, as the lining of the womb is no longer maintained by hormones, it begins to break up. This is shed with some blood and that is what your period is. You may get little or no warning of your first period, but there is nothing to be afraid of. Every girl gets them and so they are nothing to be embarrassed about either. You may also get abdominal pains or 'cramps'. If these are severe, there are various tablets available from chemists without prescription.

The entrance to the vagina, a.k.a. your twat, piddler, cunt, fanny, pussy, is part of the vulva, which is the outer genital area that you can see. The most prominent bit is the mons veneris which is the mound of hair-covered fatty tissue which covers your pubic bone. Extending from this are the labia majora, which literally means large lips. Within the folds of the labia majora are the labia minora, which means small lips. The small lips swell with blood when you get excited – over a boy not a Christmas present.

In the middle of your external organs is a small bump called the clitoris, containing the nerve endings which make sex pleasurable. Below the clitoris and above the vaginal opening is a teeny slit which is the outer opening of the urethra, through which you take a widdle. The interior of the vagina is about four or five inches long in grown women. Before puberty, it's only about one or two inches long, but then your body begins to produce oestrogen and that lengthens the vagina. The vagina ends inside you with the cervix, which is the entrance to your womb. The vaginal walls consist of smooth muscles and pink, vaguely corrugated connective tissues. The whole thing is lined with a mucous membrane called the epithelium. Normally the walls touch one another. The vagina is not simply a canal as some people think; it is an organ and it only opens up when something goes inside it.

The vagina is extremely elastic. During childbirth it can expand hugely, and the numerous folds all around your vaginal walls allow it to fit around whatever happens to be inside it, be it a tampon, a baby, a finger or a willie. All in all it's a jolly good thing to have. In the vagina, there are lots of tiny blood vessels or capillaries. A fluid derived from blood plasma constantly passes through these capillaries and then seeps through the vaginal walls keeping it moist and clean. It's therefore perfectly normal to have some mild discharge all the time. This is just your body's natural way of keeping itself clean and healthy. As long as you are clean and free from infection it is in no way unpleasant or dirty.

BOYS AND PUBERTY

In boys, the male hormones, called androgens, are responsible for the general changes. He will develop (he hopes) the typical male shape of broad shoulders, muscular chest, flat stomach, a small bottom, narrow hips and well-developed muscles in his legs and arms. He will also develop body hair and ultimately, facial hair. One of the most embarrassing things for some boys as they mature is their voice breaking. The reason this happens is that hormones cause the larynx to enlarge. This enlargement causes his vocal chords to lengthen, which in turn makes his voice sound lower. This can take anything from weeks to months and leave him a bit squeaky for a bit. Or it may go up and down in the middle of a sentence, which unfortunately he won't be able to control. Boys also sometimes develop painful lumps under their nipples. Fear not, this is due to all the activity your hormones are putting in, growing all those muscles – you're not getting a bosom.

The increased production of sperm during adolescence often causes boys to have wet dreams. They wake up and they've come all over their pyjamas. This is perfectly natural at this time. It is usually connected with a build-up of sexual excitement in a dream. There is nothing harmful or wrong about wet dreams, nor are they dangerous.

Shagging

GIRLS AND VAGINAS

When a woman becomes aroused, blood flows to her pelvic area which swells the blood vessels inside her vagina. That is what is happening when you get that feeling of warmth and that unmistakable twinge of activity inside your navy blue serge knickers. The capillaries then push much more fluid than is usual through the walls of the vagina, making it wet. When a woman is deeply aroused, the two-thirds of her vagina that are nearest to her cervix begin to expand and her womb lifts which automatically makes the vagina longer to accommodate the willie. If she reaches orgasm, the outer third of the vagina and its surrounding muscles contract rhythmically. Obviously all these responses differ from woman to woman: some have bigger muscle contractions, some get wetter.

But what exactly sets off sexual response? Morten from Aha may be an obvious answer sweeping the country. Do women become excited simply because of clitoral stimulation? Or does the inside of the vagina trigger orgasm as well? While the clitoris is the most common source of sexual pleasure in women, it isn't the only one. Some people can get stimulation because their vaginas are very, very sensitive. Some also have very sensitive breasts. So it is a good idea to communicate subtly to your boyfriend, perhaps by showing him, what triggers a nice feeling for you individually.

BOYS AND WILLIES

Between a man's legs, he has a scrotum which contains his testicles, a.k.a. balls, bollocks, nuts, goolies. The balls are the most sensitive part of a man's body, which is why it's so excruciating if you get them injured on the football pitch. It is also extremely painful to get aftershave on them. Sperm, which make babies, are manufactured in the testicles. An interesting fact about sperm is that if men were able to swim as fast as their sperm can, they'd be up a swimming pool at 60 miles an hour. Maybe Duncan Goodhew was a sperm in a previous life. When a man ejaculates, a.k.a. comes, millions of sperm in fluid pass out along the tube from his balls, up his willie and depending on the circumstances, on to the wall or inside his girlfriend. Millions of sperm are needed because only some will actually reach the egg in the first place and it takes huge numbers to break down the wall of the egg so that one can get in. Sometimes, an egg will divide itself into two, which results in identical twins. Twins can also be conceived if the woman has produced two eggs simultaneously, which are then both fertilised.

In order to get the sperm into the woman, sexual intercourse or extremely heavy petting has to take place. When a man gets very excited, he gets an erection, a.k.a. a hard-on, stonker, etc. Instead of his willie being soft, and hanging downwards, it grows considerably in size, which happens because it fills up with blood. It becomes hard and stands up at an angle in front of his body. As a youth, I always wondered why on earth it went upwards when it stuck outwards. In actual fact, the woman's vagina, a.k.a. fanny, cunt, pussy, twat, piddler, lies back inside her body at exactly the same angle as the erect willie.

THE BUSINESS

When he has a hard-on, the man could easily immediately make love and would probably quite like to. He feels a great sense of urgency. Men are easily aroused by the presence of the opposite sex or simply by the sight of a pretty girl. But the girl may not be ready yet to make love. Women are not usually as quickly aroused as their partners. Usually, they only want to make love with men they feel very close to and secure with. Although once she is ready, the woman could make love immediately, she would probably prefer quite a lot of kissing, cuddling and petting beforehand. This is known as foreplay. It is not always the man who initiates lovemaking, and if a girl feels she wants sex, there is nothing wrong with communicating that to her boyfriend, rather than waiting for him to make the first move. This is one of the benefits of being a woman today – in the old days, it was not thought proper for women to be the aggressor. In Victorian times, women who actually enjoyed sex were thought to be ill. My friend's grandparents, in fact, never even saw each other's naked bodies and made love through flaps in their starched nightgowns.

There are several positions, nay hundreds, in which a man and a woman can make love. The best-known position is the missionary, which is not in this instance a Michael Palin film. The woman lies on her back with her legs apart and either wrapped round the man's back or with her knees raised at either side of his body. The man, ludicrous as it may seem, lies face down on top of her, with his legs in between hers. He can then push his willie in and out of her body. The feeling of having his knob inside his girlfriend is extremely nice (I think this is something of an understatement). After a while, he has an orgasm, a.k.a. coming. This is a moment of intense pleasure when the sperm is launched.

The woman may or may not have an orgasm. And it is not actually necessary for reproduction that a woman does have an orgasm; she can still get pregnant if she doesn't come. It is unusual for women, particularly young women, to experience orgasm simply from intercourse alone. A woman's orgasm is believed to be caused by stimulation of the clitoris. This is a small, button-like bump approximately an inch above the entrance to her fanny (but the precise location can vary from girl to girl – though it's roughly in the same place). Some women do not experience orgasm easily, and reaching orgasm may take more time for a girl than the boy. And he will also need to experiment with her to find out what feels best.

Afterwards

Immediately after making love, a boy's willie goes soft again. There is usually a feeling of tiredness for both partners. But often girls want to spend this time with a lot of romantic chit-chat and reassuring conversation. Unfortunately, this is one of the areas where nature may have slipped up slightly, as most boys would gladly fall asleep with their mouths open and start dreaming about United winning the cup. What we have described is lovemaking between two people who love each other – the best kind but not necessarily the only kind.

Sex often gets better the more you do it with your partner. Which is why people who have been going out together are often much happier with their sex lives. It is a matter of trial and error, finding out what pleases both of you and trusting each other enough to experiment. This is not to say that things might not ever go wrong. For girls, the first time can sometimes hurt. A boy may have longed in feverish anticipation for such a long time for the moment when you make love together that when it finally arrives, he can't get a hard-on, odd as this may sound. Alternatively, it may be over so fast that you wonder if it happened at all.

It is not unusual to be a bit taken aback by seeing the calm, gentle person you've been holding hands with these last months suddenly become what seems like a crazed beast in bed. Very powerful feelings take over during sexual intercourse and that's why it's not wise to do it until you feel you can deal with them. Or, silly things might embarrass you a great deal – maybe because you are not at ease with each other yet. You might get cramp, he might be lying on your hair. Sometimes, whether sex has been good or not, girls can get emotional and tearful and boys should be very sensitive to their feelings. Equally, girls should remember that men are not all hugely confident about sex either, and need to be treated with the same care you would expect for yourself.

Questions and answers

Q What is a French kiss?

A A French kiss is also known as a deep kiss and a tongue kiss. It means that you open your mouth and allow each other's tongues to come into contact. Why is kissing such an expressive gesture? Well, just think about what you're doing. You're combining spit, lips, and tongues with someone else. It would be like kissing the dog's bottom if you didn't like them. The lips, mouth and tongue are among the most sensitive parts of your body because they are loaded with nerve endings. Kissing enables us to test taste, smell and temperature, and it feels nice too.

A good kiss should leave both people breathless but not asphyxiated. Nobody should squash their nose or bang their teeth if they can avoid it. You should also seek a happy medium between a dry kiss, like you'd have with your friends, or a slobbery one that feels like drowning. It's very difficult to learn how to kiss because everyone does it differently. Generally, however, if something is very uncomfortable or it feels like you've got a pillow over your face, something is wrong.

Q A lot of my friends sleep with boys they haven't known very long. Will they have as much fun?

A Sex as a purely recreational activity, which some people would have us believe is great, often doesn't work like that. A lot of girls may be having casual relationships but often they might not enjoy it as much as the sex to be enjoyed during one intense relationship with one person. The mental/emotional component of making love, for women, is subtle. A woman could have endless clitoral stimulation but if she is angry with her partner, embarrassed about the situation, uncomfortable or

70

worried about something entirely separate, it is unlikely that she will become aroused. Our feelings about ourselves contribute strongly to how well our sex lives go. If we feel of value as a person, we are more likely to feel we deserve sexual pleasure and other treats. If we feel attractive, we are less likely to be inhibited.

There are some things that one can do to ensure that new encounters can be pleasant ones: (1) Make sure that you're protected against pregnancy. (2) Don't think that sex will solve other problems in your life. (3) Build up your social self-confidence so that you're not just relying on being sexy. (4) Be discreet. No-one likes someone that blabs. (5) Relax and give yourself plenty of time. (6) Stay away from any situation that feels dangerous, physically or emotionally. Never be pressured into having sex until you're ready. (7) Don't waste too much time on regrets if you make an error. Everyone sometimes makes mistakes and it doesn't make you suddenly into a horrible person with no self-respect.

Q Boys only seem to be after one thing. Are they really so different from girls?

A Yes. Like a tom-cat, most boys want to complete the act and get directly to their goal with very little distractions on the way. Girls, on the other hand, would rather savour the courtship. Once aroused, the human male would like to rush towards the bed by the shortest possible route. Whereas girls tend to think that getting there's part of the fun. Girls usually want to be wooed. They like to be taken out, have their hand held, be flattered and have the sensuous feeling of being close to someone they like. All of this, for a woman, is an important prelude to lovemaking.

Q What is an erogenous zone?

A An erogenous zone is a place where you like to be touched. This is not the space behind the bike sheds but a part of your body. These can be, in boys – lips, nipples, ears, neck and of course, primarily, the knob. In girls – lips, breasts, ears, neck and of course, the obvious.

Q My girlfriend almost lets me make love to her but then at the last minute says no. Is this frustration bad for me?

A Years ago, people were familiar with the term 'blue balls'. Which meant the pain in the groin that men who have petted almost to the point of almost but not quite orgasm get. Young men pleaded with their girlfriends to have sex with them to relieve this raging agony. It is a male fiction that damage occurs. A quick wank later on will make it better. Women, too, suffer a similar pain in the groin sometimes after a long period of unconsumed sexual passion. It can be relieved in the same way.

72

Q I have not grown very tall, nor have I got much body hair. Does this mean I am not going to be a very sexy man?

A It is a myth that the more hirsute a man is, the sexier he will be. Similarly, some women believe that a man's overall build and height has something to do with the size of his knob. There is not the slightest connection. A rugged Greek god might easily have a petite chipolata sausage, whereas a small, slight type may have a great big one. The more you worry about it, the less confident you will be and the less appealing you will seem to girls. So try to build up confidence in some other area – are you funny? Charming? Artistic? Many girls like the sensitive type and feel turned off by powerful, macho types.

Q Do boys need sex more often than women?

A This is linked with the theory that men nearly always want to make love whereas women need to be in the mood. This difference in temperament has led to all the jokes about women having headaches. Men sometimes feel rejected and women, in turn, are convinced that men only think about one thing. At certain times of the month, depending on her cycle, a woman will feel sexier than at others. Whereas a man's sexual urges are not so subject to ups and downs.

  Sometimes, a girl may have her mind on other things which will distract her from the matter in hand. Another facet is that the girl might think that they are merely having a friendly conversation when, in fact, the boy is chatting her up. Then she will be shocked when she realises his real motives.

Q My boyfriend talks about sex all the time. I am sick of it.

A Boys often make the mistake of imagining that by telling a girl a really filthy joke, it is a prelude to more amorous chit-chat. It often has actually the reverse effect. But because he may have been stimulated by telling it, he imagines she will be too. Sexy talk plays a part in female arousal, but preferably within the context of a general sensual situation rather than over a beer and a packet of pork scratchings.

Q I have trouble reaching orgasm during sex. Is my clitoris too far away from my vagina?

A Although the clitoris is not in exactly the same spot in everyone, it is generally located in the front of the pubic area, protected by the labia. When it is touched and stroked, the clitoris can give a woman her deepest, most pleasurable orgasm. But steady stimulation is the key. If you and your boyfriend are having sex in the missionary position, his body may not be making contact with your clitoris consistently enough. You might be happier on top. For some women, however, no position ensures an orgasm during intercourse. They are more likely to achieve it during foreplay or if their boyfriend touches and strokes their clitoris during sex. But unlike men, women can be satisfied by intercourse without it ending in orgasm. And the more you worry about it, the less likely it is to happen.

Q I would like to be more aggressive with my boyfriend. Will it put him off?

A No. Most men do prefer to go out with a woman who is able to communicate her sexual desires. A lot of girls somehow imagine that their boyfriends have taken a course in mind-reading and know exactly what they're supposed to do and when, without being told.

Q I would like to be more soppy with my girlfriend but I am worried in case she will think I'm a cissy.

A A man who is able to cry or express his feelings is no longer laughed at in this society or thought to be in some way lacking in masculinity. Far more important than your ability to cry is your ability to be sensitive to a woman's affection.

Q My girlfriend and I would like to make love, but I have been coming before I am even inside my girlfriend. Is there anything we can do?

A One technique is called stop/start. The man stops the stimulation just before he thinks he's going to come. Then his girlfriend can touch him again as soon as his hard-on has subsided a little. This technique is not always successful at first, but can be patiently learned by most men. You could also try thinking about something completely different like cricket scores, and also remember that as you get older, and more used to making love with your girlfriend, it will not be such a problem.

Q I frequently get hard-ons during the day. Is this normal?

A Some years ago, there was a very detailed survey of people's sex lives and responses conducted by a man called Kinsey. You may have heard his name because what he found out is still quoted often. He found twenty-three physical and forty-one non-sexual sources of erotic response among younger adolescent boys. Any number of these may be carried into adult life. They included: riding a horse, peeing, driving a fast car, getting in a lift, anger, watching or playing exciting games, and dreams. So there is nothing unusual about you.

Q What is the difference between my sexual fantasies and my girlfriend's?

A Your girlfriend's probably concern something she has already experienced whereas yours may go beyond this to what you would like to experience in the future. However, the new sexual freedom is beginning to make a difference and women feel more at ease and more able to let their imaginations roam.

Q What can I do about painful periods?

A (1) Know what is going on so you are not anxious.
(2) There are tablets now which will ease cramps and you can get these from your chemist over the counter. (3) A good walk or a bike ride can often help the pain. (4) If it's really bad, a hot water bottle resting on your tummy will make it all feel much better.

6 *Contraception*

From an early age, women are taught to be very aware of their reproductive systems, how they work and what the different things that will happen to their body will feel like. Men aren't taught at all, and consequently they grow up knowing far less about their own bodies and women's bodies than women do. This imbalance in their education tends to continue even after people are quite grown up.

Most women, even when they are perfectly healthy, should go for check-ups through which they will learn more about their own bodies, and more about contraception. Men, on the other hand, particularly if they are fit, very rarely go to the doctor and men's magazines are mainly concerned with bouncing bosoms from Bolton rather than in-depth articles on the virtues of the smear test. So many men today still know little or nothing about birth control. Many young men today are insecure and quite shy about this aspect of sex and, in some ways, talking to their girlfriends about contraception seems even more intimate than the actual act itself. So they'd rather avoid discussing it and leave it completely up to the girl, the theory being, she's the one who'll have the baby, it's up to her to protect herself. Many young women, on the other hand, are equally shy about the subject of contraception. But if you are mature enough to make love, you are mature enough to face the responsibility of contraception. For the above reasons (and many others) it is not wise to rely simply on your boyfriend taking that responsibility. The boys who do ask you about contraception and whether you are protected usually manage

to pluck up the courage only after you have already had sex with them.

In some cases, they may not want to share in the responsibility of contraception because to some men it signifies a sense of commitment for which they are not ready. By not confronting this issue they feel they are allowing themselves an escape hatch. Rightly or wrongly, many women feel that if the boy is taking no interest at all in contraception, it somehow symbolises a lack of caring for her. But men's seeming thoughtlessness about birth control doesn't necessarily mean an absence of love and caring, it's often just insecurity and inexperience.

That's being nice about it. A lot of boys are not in the slightest bit interested in contraception and merely want to get straight on with the shagging. No couple who do not long for a baby to make their family complete should ever risk having an unwanted child. And these days, there are enough methods to ensure that a reliable one will suit.

It is no use avoiding the subject of contraception because you are worried that you will appear too keen, or that there is in some way something 'fast' about being already prepared. There is still a teenage romantic myth of sex being something that sweeps you away dramatically, over which you have no control. As always, it helps to know each other well and establish a rapport. This way you can talk about contraception. Durex is not something you can talk about while in the throes of passion and although it may seem calculating to discuss contraception before the actual event, afterwards is inevitably too late.

Feeling relaxed in the knowledge that you have an effective contraceptive is also going to mean a better sex life.

Who to turn to

This is not the time to be discussing the moral issues inherent in young people making love. The point is, if you have reached the stage of making love, you must have contraception. The Gillick Case made many young women afraid to approach their doctors or family planning clinics because they were worried the doctors would either tell their parents or just turn them away. It is unlikely that being turned away from a clinic that would provide you with contraception would automatically mean that your ardour has been dampened. All it did was make it more likely that teenagers were indulging in unprotected sex. In truth, very few doctors were informing parents – but still, lots of frightened girls probably made love without protection rather than risk their parents finding out. Since the reversal of the decision there need now be no worry that a family doctor will break your confidence to tell someone something you regard as private.

If you can possibly broach the subject with your parents first, before turning to a doctor for contraceptive help, you will avoid the inevitable confrontation when your mother finds out that – without her knowledge – you have been having sex. This can be a very traumatic time. Remember, if your parents have had an active sex life for the duration of their marriage, your mother is likely to be something of an authority on the subject of con- traception. She will be able to tell you first-hand the practicalities of some of the different methods. But it is not an easy subject to raise over the family dinner table as you will always be your mummy's little baby. It is just as hard for them to imagine you having sex as it is for you to imagine them indulging in it.

Visiting your family doctor for contraceptive advice, when he's treated you for mumps, etc., since you could barely walk, can also be nerve-wracking. Listed in your Yellow Pages under F for Family Planning are clinics to whom you can turn for advice and free contraceptive supplies. These clinics are very discreet and see literally hundreds of thousands of teenagers (many of them under sixteen) every year. They know exactly how nervous you will feel visiting them for the first time and will do everything they can to relax you. They will ask questions but they won't make any moral judgements – their goal is simply to ensure that no girl has an unwanted pregnancy.

What happens at the clinic

You might want to take your best friend or even your boyfriend along with you on your first visit to the Family Planning clinic. If you have someone to chat to while you are waiting, it will help to make the whole experience less nerve-wracking – even though there is really nothing to be afraid of.

This first visit to the clinic will probably go as follows: You will be asked to give details of your address, date of birth, family doctor, etc. Don't worry – they aren't going to get in touch with your parents or your doctor, they simply need this information for their files. They aren't going to write to you at home.

Initially, you will probably have a chat with a nurse, who will discuss with you the various different contraceptive options available to you. Between you, you will probably decide on a method. If you are going to take the Pill, she will weigh you and take your blood pressure – a few women, who are very overweight or who have a family history of high blood pressure or thrombosis might not be suited to this method at all. There are plenty of other options if this is true in your case, so please don't be frightened to disclose if there is such a history in your family – it is in the best interest of your health to answer all questions honestly.

You will then see the doctor, who will probably give you an internal examination and check your breasts for lumps. Everyone's worried about that. It is quick, though it may be uncomfortable and, depending on how nervous you are, sometimes a tiny bit painful. The doctor will ask you to lie down on a bed with your legs apart and bent, but keeping your feet on the bed. Then he or she will put on a transparent plastic glove and reach inside to feel that everything is normal and that there is no inflammation. Then the doctor will insert a metal speculum which can feel very cold and isn't the sort of thing you would want to happen every day. But it means that he or she can check properly that everything is OK, and also take a smear. He scrapes a tiny bit from your cervix (you can barely feel this at all) and will send this off to a laboratory for analysis. It is extremely rare to find any abnormalities in the smears of very young women, but you should have a regular six-monthly or yearly smear because it can act as an early warning for anything that might go wrong in the future and can be nipped in the bud with some fast treatment. The doctor will also probably check your breasts for any unusual lumps and bumps – and this is something you should learn to do at home each month. It is not unusual to feel very vulnerable and even a bit weepy during internal examinations.

Then the doctor will prescribe the contraception that you, the nurse and the doctor have decided is most appropriate. They will write out a prescription and make absolutely sure that you understand how to use the contraceptive. If you are unclear about their instructions, now is the time to ask. It's no good trying to figure it out when you get home, and in order to be fully effective, all contraceptives must be used according to instructions. When I was a child I once walked into a small literary soirée my mother was throwing wearing her diaphragm on my head. This just illustrates my point about how confusing some articles of contraception can appear.

They will probably ask you to make an appointment to come back in a month to make sure that everything is working out OK. After that, you will need to go back every six months, or earlier if you run out of supplies or have more queries.

What are the different contraceptives available?

THE PILL

By taking contraceptive pills, a woman stops herself ovulating. She can make love with very little chance of having a baby as long as she doesn't forget to take it at the required time every day. No girl should rely on the Pill unless she absolutely understands the instructions. Nor should you ever obtain Pills from anyone other than your doctor or clinic.

There are many different brands of Pill, but two main kinds. The oestrogen/progesterone 'combined' Pill is one which you take every day for twenty-one days and then stop for seven. During the break, you will have some bleeding rather like a period, but it is not a proper period. It will often be lighter and shorter than those you had before you went on the Pill. For this reason, some doctors prescribe the Pill for girls with painful, heavy or irregular periods. Sometimes, particularly at first, you may get 'spotting' or breakthrough bleeding. You lose a small amount of blood, usually in the middle of your cycle. Also available is the 'progesterone only' Pill, which you should take all the time with a period of breakthrough bleeding each month. It is very important with this Pill to take it at the identical time every day.

If you miss taking the Pill, or have a stomach upset or are taking some other kind of medicine, you can risk becoming pregnant. So if this happens, it is wise to use some kind of other contraceptive in addition, for the rest of your cycle. Nowadays, doctors tend to tell you to start taking the Pill on the first day of your period and you will then be protected thereafter.

Taken according to instructions, the Pill is the most effective method of contraception available to women. The first one you take might not turn out to be absolutely suitable, but if you feel sick, or bloated or tired, tell your doctor and he or she can prescribe an alternative brand. There are some girls who never feel right taking the Pill, for whatever reason, and here are some alternatives for them.

THE CAP

For the cap, or diaphragm, a woman must go to her doctor as these come in all different sizes and must be fitted. Once the woman has got the knack of putting it inside herself, she can use it whenever she makes love. It is important to practise as there is a certain knack involved in inserting the cap. The cap is rapidly coming back into fashion as many women don't like the idea of taking the Pill, especially if they don't have a very regular sex life. The advantage of the cap is, you only use it when you need it.

The cap, or diaphragm as it is also known, is a small rubber saucer that fits over the neck of the womb making a barrier that sperm cannot get through. It has to be inserted just before you make love and must be used in conjunction with a spermicidal jelly or foam, which your Family Planning clinic will also supply. Experts disagree about exactly how many hours before intercourse it is safe to insert the diaphragm. Their figures range from 2–3 hours. If you are not able to put it in a few hours beforehand, compensate by using more spermicide. You should squirt four thick strips inside of the diaphragm and add an extra measure around the rim. How long to leave the diaphragm in after intercourse is a stricter rule. It should stay in place at least six to eight hours after you last made love. This gives the spermicide ample time to destroy sperms.

It is not something you can simply leave knocking around in the bottom of your handbag as, obviously, if it ever gets torn it is of no use to you. It has to be well cared for. This consists of cleaning in tepid water with a plain soap, gently towelling it dry and dusting it with cornstarch before returning it to a cool, dry place. No matter how much you have cared for it, it should be thrown away if it looks thin or worn out in any way when you hold it up to the light.

Although the cap is a perfect form of contraception for many women, some women have experienced a range of mechanical problems. If you are in a hurry, it is sometimes difficult to insert as you are too flustered. Also, you can experience dislodgment during intercourse. Dislodgment means it may not be fitting you perfectly, and therefore not doing its job properly. If changing sizes doesn't work you should switch to another method of birth control.

THE SPONGE

Like a diaphragm with jelly, the contraceptive sponge works by blocking the cervix and by the sperm-killing ingredients. One difference between the two methods is that the spermicide in the sponge must be activated before insertion by wetting it and then squeezing it. The next step, which is inserting the sponge high up inside yourself, can be even trickier. The sponge can be bought over the counter or prescribed by your doctor who will show you how to use it properly. Estimates vary about its effectiveness, and it is probably best not to rely on it alone for contraception, as it seems to become more effective the more practice you get. Practice can be hard to come by. Although it is better than no contraceptive protection at all, it's probably best used, for instance, if you have missed a Pill and want to be doubly sure.

THE COIL

The coil, or intra-uterine device (IUD), can only be fitted by your doctor. But it is almost unheard of for a doctor to fit it in a young girl. They prefer to prescribe it for women in a long-standing relationship, preferably women who have already had a child or completed their families. It is a small t- or seven-shaped piece of plastic, usually with copper coiled round it, which fits inside your womb, with strings hanging down through your cervix. It can stay in place for two to three years but needs to be checked every six months by your doctor. Women should also regularly check that it is in place by feeling for the strings in their vaginas. Strange as it sounds, nobody quite knows how it works but its origins go back as far as Egyptian times. It probably prevents a fertilised egg from implanting itself in the wall of the uterus.

The coil is probably one of the easiest forms of contraception, since once it's in you don't have to think about it any more. But it can cause very bad period pains, extra-heavy bleeding and leave you susceptible to infection. Occasionally, it can be the cause of an ectopic, or tubal pregnancy, which occurs outside the womb in the Fallopian tubes and can be dangerous. In a very small number of cases, there is a risk of perforation of the womb when the coil is inserted. And doctors are very reluctant to prescribe it to any woman who is at risk of contracting a sexual infection, as it is possible that she could become sterile. It is less reliable than the Pill as it is possible to get pregnant with the coil in place, or for it to drop out – unlikely as it may sound – without you realising.

85

Also known as rubbers, johnnies, sheaths or Durex, which is actually a brand name but, rather like Hoover, has become the word everyone uses. The condom, rather like twenty-inch flares, platform-soled boots and Donny Osmond purple hats, has a way of becoming, every few years, enormously unfashionable and the topic of some derision. Not at present. The condom is enjoying an enormous resurgence of popularity. This is partly because of recent media coverage of the variously sexually contracted diseases, which the condom to a certain extent can help protect one against. Used every time it is also a very effective form of contraception.

The Durex (or any other brand) is a sheath of very thin rubber. It is rolled on over the man's willie, so that when he is having sex, it is almost impossible for his sperm to get out, as it is all trapped at the end, unpleasant as that may sound. To make even more sure of its efficiency, you or your partner can keep the sperm in their place by pressing the rim of the rubber firmly against the base of his willie after he's come. And it is also wise for the girl to use a spermicide. Human error isn't the only thing that influences their effectiveness. While rubbers rarely rip, here are some just-in-case precautions to keep in mind – you should keep them in a cool spot, not in your wallet for long periods of time as they can be damaged by heat and perish. Don't use one that is sticky or brittle. You should remember to unfurl it down the willie, not yank it on, as this might tear it. If you do find it has broken during intercourse, get your girlfriend to use an extra squirt of spermicide. She should also add more every time you have sex, and if she's using foam, make sure she shakes the can well. Many doctors feel that when using a spermicide, to be on the safe side, you should use it no more than half an hour beforehand. They should not be used on their own as they give nothing like sufficient protection.

Condoms can of course be bought in any chemist, from slot machines and from barbers. A lot of boys and some girls may not wish to use one. The reasons for this are that condoms have a horrible tendency to be hilarious. Also, they can interfere with sensitivity. There is no way of getting round this, but that in fact may be useful for anyone who suffers from premature ejaculation. Manufacturers are lately perfecting the process of making condoms thinner than ever without losing their effectiveness – as thin as 0.03 millimetres. But men still tend to say that it is like taking a shower with a raincoat on or having a bath with one's socks on.

THE RHYTHM METHOD

This is a method which, since it is 'natural', is accepted by the Catholic church. The only time that an egg can be fertilised is after it has been released from the ovary and is travelling through the Fallopian tube towards the womb. So a couple then avoids lovemaking from the date ovulation occurred and until the egg reaches the womb and menstruation starts. As you can see, this system relies on the woman knowing exactly when the egg is released from the ovary, and while it sounds simple in theory, in practice it is *not* a foolproof method of contraception. Your local doctor or Family Planning clinic will give you clear instructions on how to work out when your safe time is, but it will entail scrupulous attention to details – taking your temperature daily and charting its fluctuations. What should happen is that your temperature will drop just before ovulation and then rise sharply when ovulation actually occurs and maintain that rise until your period starts.

If you have decided that you want to use the rhythm method, be aware that doctors do not advise it. Also be aware that you will have to take several different charts to ensure that your calculations are regular and correct. You should also remember that any kind of stress or illness may alter your dates.

THE BILLINGS METHOD

This is another 'natural' method of contraception. But, like the Rhythm method, the Billings method also depends on careful calculations. You will also need to be taught how to interpret the different stages. It works by charting the state of your cervical and vaginal secretions, which change as ovulation occurs. The risks are as substantial as with the Rhythm method, and unless you are prepared for pregnancy, neither method is recommended.

COITUS INTERRUPTUS

This is the name given to the man pulling out just before he comes. Supposedly they then get all the pleasure of intercourse without the risk. This is a very chancey thing to do, since well before a man comes, small quantities of sperm escape, and as we all know, it only takes one to make you pregnant. It is also possible that the man may not be able to withdraw in time. Emotionally, it is also frustrating for both partners and really should be avoided.

Research has shown that the most likely times for a woman to become slapdash about contraception are during times of stress: (1) After a pregnancy scare or an abortion, odd as it may seem. The woman probably believes that she won't be interested in sex and therefore won't need contraception. But research shows that a person or a situation can change her mind and she will be unprepared for this change of heart. (2) At the beginning or the end of a relationship. (3) Family and social crises, exams, moving, or an illness in the family.

How to choose a contraceptive for your lifestyle

THE PILL MAY BE A GOOD CHOICE IF . . .

(1) You have sex often and unpredictably. (2) You don't like messing with birth control just before you're going to make love. (3) It bothers you to touch your sexual parts.

IT MAY NOT BE SUCH A GOOD CHOICE IF . . .

(1) You have trouble sticking to a schedule. (2) You don't like the idea of taking chemicals or hormones. (3) You don't have sex often. (4) You often use alcohol or drugs.

A DIAPHRAGM MAY BE A GOOD CHOICE IF . . .

(1) You don't want protection all the time, just when you need it. (2) You feel OK about planning ahead for sex. (3) You don't mind touching your sexual parts.

IT MAY NOT BE SUCH A GOOD IDEA IF . . .

(1) It bothers you to touch yourself. (2) You don't like fiddling around with birth control just before making love. (3) You tend to lose or gain ten to fifteen pounds (which may mean you need to change your diaphragm size).

Contraception questions and answers

Q Are some rubbers safer than others?

A Yes. Always make sure that the rubber you buy has a 'kite mark' on the packet, which indicates it has been tested and meets the strict standards set by the British Standards Institute.

Q Is there a perfect method of contraception?

A No. Very often, finding a contraceptive which you feel at home with is a matter of trial and error. You might need several visits to the Family Planning clinic to find one which is most suitable for you and your partner.

Q How do we use a rubber?

A (1) Remember, do not stretch, inflate or even unroll a rubber before you're ready to use it. When your partner's willie is erect, the rubber should be pressed against the end and unrolled towards the base. If a woman is doing this for her partner she needs to be careful of her fingernails. If a rubber should slip off during intercourse – and you should be alert to this possibility – immediately use a spermicidal foam or jelly.

Q Can my boyfriend re-use his rubbers?

A Except as a very last resort, you should never re-use one. If you do have to, you should carefully wash it, rinse it and blot it dry, and if possible powder it with cornstarch and then re-roll it. If you still feel like sex after this it will be a miracle.

Q What is a French Tickler?

A There are some notorious and exotic brands of rubbers now available in various colours and textures. Not surprisingly, these special kinds of rubber have a tendency to appear somewhat silly. The idea behind them is that by being corrugated, they give extra stimulation to the woman. But this is hard to prove: (1) since nobody wants to admit they use them, and (2) because most of the woman's nerve endings are in her clitoris rather than in her vagina.

Q What should I do if I have forgotten to bring any form of contraception?

A Don't have sex. Go for a walk instead.

Q What happens if I miss a Pill?

A If you are on the Pill, practically the only way for you to get pregnant is if you miss taking it. If you are on a low-dose Pill (make sure your doctor explains which one he has prescribed for you), then first of all find out if it was from the middle of your cycle – days 10–15, counting the first day of your last period as Day 1. If you miss a Pill from these middle days, you will definitely need some back-up contraception, like Durex and spermicide, for the remainder of your cycle, until your next period. With other types of Pill, which work by keeping your hormone levels in the body elevated over a period of time, not simply day-to-day, simply take the Pill you have missed as soon as you remember. If you miss two days, or more, then you will definitely need some other form of contraception for the rest of your cycle until your next period.

Q I ate a dodgy Chinese last night and was ill. My friend says I could get pregnant. Is she right?

A You will only get pregnant if you had sex as well. Chinese meals alone are unlikely to do it. But yes, any kind of stomach upset – vomiting or diarrhoea – can put you at risk. So it is best to use a cap, or condom, for the rest of your cycle.

Q I am going on holiday. I don't want to get my period while I'm away. Can I just go on taking my Pill?

A Every now and then, delaying your period by continuing to take the Pill won't do you any harm. As long as it's not done often enough to confuse your Pill-taking routine – such as for a special event like a holiday or weekend away – then you'll be fine.

Q I keep reading that the Pill is dangerous. How true is that?

A It is hard to tell how dangerous any drug is as new research is constantly being done. But it is wise to look into the history of the Pill to see how things have developed. In the 1940s scientists realised they could make synthetic versions of oestrogen and progesterone. Twenty years later, birth control pills were made available. But soon afterwards, serious side-effects began to be realised. The Pill was blamed for causing blood clots, strokes, high blood pressure and benign liver tumours. However, some of these early studies have been found to have errors, so some Pill perils were exaggerated. But it is clear now that probably the thing causing the problems with the early Pill was the high hormone dose it contained. Hormone levels in the Pill have been dramatically reduced, even though its efficiency keeps it the most effective contraceptive available. The present trend is for a low-dose Pill, which contains about a third of the oestrogen in the early Pill.

At the moment, most doctors think that if you are healthy, under thirty-five and with no history of heart disease, diabetes, liver disease or excess weight, and you are using one of the low-dose pills, the risk of serious side-effects is very small. It is true to say that every time there is a Pill 'scare' in the papers, loads of girls go straight off it. After that, of course, doctors' surgeries are full of girls who had unprotected sex and find themselves pregnant. If a Pill scare worries you so much that you want to stop taking it, go and see your doctor for an alternative method and genuine medical, rather than media, advice on the subject.

Q Are there any advantages, apart from contraceptive ones, in being on the Pill?

A Some women find that they are less prone to spots if they are on the Pill. Other women find their bosoms get a bit bigger. Various studies have suggested also that oral contraceptive users may have less risk than other women of developing ovarian cancer, endometrial cancer and rheumatoid arthritis. Research into the relationship between Pill use and breast cancers has left some researchers thinking that oral contraceptives might decrease your risk, while other researchers will only say that Pills don't increase it. Also, Pill users have lower rates of pelvic inflammatory diseases. These diseases can cause tubal pregnancies, and infertility. They have fewer ovarian cysts, lighter period pains and less anaemia because they are not losing so much blood. This allows their bodies to store more iron.

Q I have found that I am very 'dry' since I started using the Pill. Can this be so?

A Some girls find that they produce less lubrication when they are on the Pill – occasionally, quite dramatically so. The answer is either to indulge in longer foreplay, or to use a lubricating jelly such as KY, available from your chemist. It is also sometimes true that contact lens wearers start to have problems when they go on the Pill, because they produce less fluid in the eyes. You might have to weigh up whether you want this effective contraceptive and wear specs, or whether you'd rather keep your contact lenses and use a different contraceptive. Although I have never found any truth in Dorothy Parker's little epithet that men never make passes at girls who wear glasses.

Q Do condoms come in different sizes?

A Condoms are a one-size-fits-all contraceptive. They adapt to fit all sizes so there is no worry about a condom being too big or too small, although I think they should all be marked extra large to give boys extra confidence.

Q I live in a small village and there is no Family Planning clinic for miles. So I need to go to our family doctor. He is a friend of my parents. Can I be sure he won't tell my mum and dad?

A Doctors take an oath called the Hippocratic Oath when they qualify which obliges them to keep their patients' confidence at all times and not disclose information about your medical record to anyone other than to a hospital. Many girls get worried at the thought that their doctor will immediately ring their mother and tell her they've been shagging. But this is not the case and he could in fact get into big trouble for betraying your confidence. So while it might be embarrassing, it is private.

Q I am a Catholic. My boyfriend and I want to make love. I want to use the rhythm method. Is it safe?

A It is extremely unlikely that if you are still in your teens, your cycle will have settled down enough to work out exactly when you are most likely to get pregnant, and conversely, when is 'safe'. To be perfectly honest, you are going against the doctrine of your church by having sex at all, so you may as well save yourself any heartache and family upset which would result from getting pregnant by making sure that you are adequately fixed up with contraception beforehand.

7 *The family way*

The best way to avoid pregnancy is to use contraception or not to have sex. But accidents can and do happen.

Having a baby is a wonderful thing to happen to a woman. It is one of the most thrilling, and satisfying events in her life. However, like many other major steps women take during their lives, pregnancy, probably more than any other, needs to be taken at the right time. It can be the most fulfilling experience if you are in love and in a settled relationship, and ready not only to settle down but to feel unselfish enough always to think of somebody else first. But for every one romantic or idealised point about having a child, I promise you there are ten that are mundane practicalities.

A baby isn't just an extension of the fact that you feel you're in love with your boyfriend. Nor is it just a good way of getting a council flat. Nor is it a way of giving yourself some identity – you may not have a job, but you're 'so and so's mother'. A baby starts out a small creature that relies on you every second of the day to wash it, feed it, entertain it, know when it wants to go to sleep and generally be a loving mind reader. A small baby cannot be left alone, so you will probably find it hard to go out at night unless you have a babysitter. When it gets bigger, things may get even more difficult. If you are having your child for motives other than a desire to create a family unit, building on a stable relationship, you may find that it gets tougher as your baby gets older. What started as a small baby that you could cuddle and play with will turn into a little tyrant that needs to be watched all the time and can demolish a room in seconds. If you are not old enough

yourself to cope with the strong will and endless tantrums of a two- and three-year-old, the whole thing may seem like a miserable mistake which has robbed you of years in which you could have been doing all the things the older parent does to prepare him or herself for living with their child.

Babies are incredibly expensive. They are also not usually like something out of a Pampers advert. They do not waft into bed with you, gazing up at you and murmuring 'Mummy. Mummy, I love you' as soon as they are born. It is a frequently made mistake, especially among very young girls, to imagine a baby is just someone they have to love them. Rather like getting a boyfriend, it takes a while for a baby to become all the things you may have imagined it would be, and your feelings of distress and disappointment will be magnified by the fact that unless it is a decision you have reached for good reasons, however nebulous that might sound, you will feel cheated by a child who had absolutely no say in the matter at all.

But accidents do happen, and you will have to make a decision if you do discover that what most teenagers imagine is the worst thing possible has actually happened to you. You must always remember that you do have choices.

How to tell if you are pregnant

One is constantly reading in the papers about women who are about to go out to the Yacht Club annual dinner or the Rotary Club ball when they nip upstairs in their full-length blue polyester dancing outfit to have a quick widdle and inevitably come downstairs having given birth to a bouncing baby next to the laundry basket. I, like you, used to sneer in utter derision at these women, who had managed to experience an entire nine month pregnancy while still maintaining they had bad wind or had put on a bit of weight. I no longer sneer at these people, for two reasons: the first is that I have noticed the astonishing ability, particularly of frightened, under-age mothers, to completely ignore the symptoms of their pregnancy, hiding it both from themselves and their parents and continuing to live under an illusion: 'It can't possibly be happening to me, if I don't think about it, it will go away.' The second reason is because I myself thought I had a trapped nerve in my back and didn't realise I was pregnant until I was almost five months gone.

Here is an article that I wrote for *Cosmopolitan* magazine:

This morning I sat perusing my Sunday papers, and I was moved almost to shedding a few tears over a large colour portrait of the newly-stuffed body of Guy the Gorilla. Not for the usual sentimental reasons but because, even at the crack of dawn over a bowl of Ready Brek, I spotted staggering similarities between my body and Guy's. In my present pregnant tetchy state, Guy and I appear to have been visiting the same taxidermist and are probably both destined to spend eternity gazing mournfully down at a large beer gut with a triple F cup resting on top and two short fat legs sticking out at the bottom.

When pregnant, you tend to spend a lot of time thinking there's something seriously wrong with you because, contrary to what you've been told, you don't feel much like skipping around in a floaty white nightie picking daisies and spreading little beams of happiness. This is one of the first large fiberoonies you'll be told. And now, big girls, woman to woman, I'll discuss a couple of other whoppers-I-have-heard . . .

'A Pregnant Woman Is A Thing of Beauty.' Most of the people believing this also harbour secret longings to write to men's magazines that advertise for one-legged women with their ears in plaster casts for unique friendship and travel. Most women will have to accept that they are beautiful 'fluffy lickul bunny wunnies' only to their lovers – fathers-to-be luckily being blind and irrational people prepared to undertake futile expeditions like trying to find a pepperoni in Clapham at 3 a.m.

Everyone else wonders why you've wedged yourself into that pinafore with a greased shoe horn, why you keep falling asleep and why, as someone noted, 'your spiritual glow seems to manifest itself in spots.' Quite. Having been told I'd have a complexion like a radiating peach, for several weeks my face actually resembled an adventure playground for dermatologists. On the other hand, it does make one realise that there is life after six and a half stone. I was amazed when men acted like rampant animals, desperate for a feel of my paunch. They became unbelievably gallant, but then again they didn't know that I had taken to walking backwards into the bedroom wearing winceyette blackout curtains. Nor did they guess that lurking beneath my Emanuel maternity frocks was a tummy that did aerobics every time I ate a wine gum. One man who was telling me – much to my joy – how pregnant women were the essence of femininity and vulnerability, added earnestly, 'Did you know you've had a sweet little moustache since you've been expecting the prawn?' Girlfriends thought it very womanly. One friend, gazing in wonder at my chest which had expanded from twenty-nine inches to ludicrous proportions, said 'With that chest, maybe you should do some sexy pictures like Nastassia Kinski did with the python!'

Which brings me to another old chestnut: 'Think Beautiful Thoughts.' Barbara Cartland claims that when she was pregnant with Raine she set aside an hour a day for lying on a chaise longue thinking beautiful thoughts. I spent the first three months of my pregnancy behaving like a cross between Tony Perkins in the last ten minutes of *Psycho* and Montgomery Clift after his car accident. If anyone spoke to me I either gave them a good slapping or cried loudly till my face went puce. All this fuss depends of course on your knowing that the stork is winging his way to you clutching the prawn. I wasn't aware for some months that this was the Impending Event that was making me feel so lousy – giving the lie to that other statement one hears: 'You Know The Minute You're Pregnant.'

My doctor's office looks as though war photographer Donald McCullin decorated it for him in return for lancing a boil. Not for him the usual displays of comforting certificates. Next to the bed is a photo of the wailing wall and above the life supply of *Truss Monthly* is a large colour photo of a man with one leg grinning gamely and waving his crutch. On the first visit to discover the source of my undiagnosed malaise, he suggested that I stop Hoovering as I was ill from stress and excess work. I refrained from mentioning that my life was one long dress-fitting, punctuated by bouts of creative angst in Fortnum's tea-rooms. But by the second visit, my beloved was making secret phone calls to friends saying I was in the throes of a raging nervous breadvan.

On the third visit, my doctor said my colon was twisted, and by the fourth – when my chest entered the room before me – he said I was eating too much due to stress and I had a trapped nerve in my back. Enuff is enuff, I thought, and went to stay with my friend Carol in the country, occupying myself on the train by watching my chest grow. Carol diagnosed my condition on the station platform. After asking if I'd de-liberately inflated my trousers with a lilo pump, she lowered her voice to shriek and said 'Bleeding obvious, innit?' Next thing I knew, five test tubes were perched on the bath with a note saying quaintly: Piss in these.

Carol's bathroom is a Kentish rendering of the golden age of the Golden Empire. If you fail to move with the agility of Sebastian Coe, you are in danger of trapping your rear end in the electrically operated loo seat. The curtains shut if you sit on the bed and water starts running out of a gold-plated swan's head if you tread on the bath mat. So you can imagine what it was like at six in the morning trying to pee into test tubes with one foot on the onyx soap dish and one on the swan-shaped loo roll dispenser that plays the *Marseillaise*. The Venetian blinds were going up and down and I thought I might end up by launching the Space Shuttle.

'You'll Never Forget the Moment When You Find Out.' This is actually true. I can remember being pulled from my prone position, crying into the shagpile with shock, by Carol's husband who was shouting somewhat bafflingly 'This is the

100

greatest day of my life!' I then rang the father-to-be in New York where it was four in the morning. An almighty crash on his end of the phone heralded the sinking in of the big news and two hundred roses winged their way to *chez* Chris and Carol. Being a somewhat shallow person, I must admit that the arrival of a large number of floral tributes and a fitting at the Emanuels did great things for the morale. Having got through the loathsome first few months without even knowing what was happening, even I – possibly the grumpiest girl in the western hemisphere – have to admit it has its good points.

I had a scan last week. I lay there averting my eyes from the tum, which is now the colour of a dead trout because I haven't been on a sunbed, and they covered it in what looked like French dressing so the scan skidded across it like Torville and Dean. For the first time I got a glimpse of the prawn and it looked just like the material for *Cosmopolitan* covers in twenty years time. It already has film star appeal. In my Polaroid it looks exactly like ET.

If you are very worried about being pregnant, which most young girls are, you may find that this can delay your period on its own. On the other hand, if you are worried about being pregnant, the sooner you find out the better. There are now kits available from chemists which enable you to do your own pregnancy test as little as ten days after a missed period, provided you stick carefully to the instructions. This should be swiftly followed by a visit to the doctor for confirmation and advice. But it is important to remember that pregnancy tests are not infallible. If the test is positive, go to the doctor or Family Planning clinic at once, even if the news is unwelcome. And if the test is negative, repeat it in a few days to make doubly certain.

Here are some of the symptoms which you should be looking out for if you suspect that you might be pregnant. But every woman varies and you may have very few symptoms at first.

1 Missing periods: When the egg is fertilised, the body immediately prepares a place for it by enriching the womb lining, which provides nourishment and protection. However, some women still have a period after a pregnancy has begun, though the bleeding is usually of shorter duration than usual. As the pregnancy grows, it fills the womb and the lining provides a base for the placenta. From this time on, no blood should be lost at all and you will get no further periods until several weeks after the pregnancy is over.

2 Morning sickness: Hormone levels alter dramatically when you are first pregnant. And the mother may find it hard to adjust to the massive doses of oestrogen and progesterone which are in her system. Then she feels sick. This can happen at any time of the day although nausea and/or vomiting can seem worse in the morning. To combat nausea, continue eating but try and avoid the obvious things like fatty or spicy foods. Eat little and often. Sit up slowly when you wake up and take things easy. If you are not managing to keep food down see your doctor immediately.

3 You may have sore breasts and you may also notice that they are getting steadily larger.

4 Expanding waistline. Even early on, you may find that your body lays down extra fat to prepare itself for pregnancy.

5 Tiredness. Extreme tiredness often takes many newly pregnant women by surprise. She may wish to sleep all day but this tiredness does pass.

6 Another sign of pregnancy is needing to widdle frequently. This is because your womb is enlarging which puts pressure on your bladder.

Your alternatives

When you find out you are pregnant your most basic choices are whether you are going to keep your child or have an abortion. If you choose to keep it, you will then be faced with another decision – whether to bring the baby up yourself or have it adopted.

Before making any decision, the first thing you should do is see your doctor or go to the Family Planning clinic to make sure you *are* pregnant, and not work yourself up into a frenzy. Then you will have to face the fact that you must tell your parents. There is no parent on earth who is *not* going to throw a shit fit when you tell them. But parents have a lucky way of loving their children, regardless of what is happening and what they have done, and you may find your greatest source of advice and support could easily be your parents. At this time, while you are deciding what to do, the more people who can give you sensible, unbiased advice the better. I say un- biased because there are many clinics today run by groups, such as Right to Life, whose only aim is to get you to keep the child regardless of whether it is wanted or not. Many of these groups running clinics will show you very distressing photo- graphs and maybe even films of abortions.

You also have to discuss the subject very carefully with your boyfriend, because it is also his child and this is a very difficult and emotional time for him as well. The more supportive you can be of each other the better.

ABORTION

People's attitudes to abortion are often very different and for many people it is a hard subject to discuss because it is so emotionally charged. Even if you cannot morally approve of the idea of abortion, it is hard not to agree with a woman's right to choose in what can be a frightening situation. Some people, including the Catholic church, still think that abortion for any reason is murder. They consider it murder even if it is an abortion that is necessary to safeguard the mother's health. Others argue that abortion, if done early

103

enough, – is not murder because the foetus is not yet a person. People could – and do – argue endlessly about when a foetus becomes a person. But since there is no way of deciding when the foetus starts to have a right to live, and when it is still just part of the mother that she can dispose of at will, it is probably better to settle the issue by accepting the decision of the mother.

This decision should be made as early as she can possibly manage. The later on in a pregnancy that an abortion is performed, the more complicated, horrific and also emotionally disturbing it is – whereas an abortion performed in the first three months is a simple operation.

Under British law, an induced or therapeutic abortion can only be carried out if two doctors state that, having examined the pregnant woman, they feel that continuation of her pregnancy will seriously harm her physical and mental health or that of her existing children or that there is a strong risk that if the child was to be born, it would suffer serious mental or physical handicaps. The attitude of doctors to make that judgment can vary, and it is often coloured by their moral stance. Doctors at a Family Planning clinic or at one of the British Pregnancy Advisory Service clinics are used to dealing with worried, pregnant girls all the time and may be better able to understand the pressure that you are under. The form recommending an abortion must then be signed by two doctors, one being the gynaecologist who is going to carry out the operation. The operation must then be performed either in hospital or in a specially approved and licensed clinic under a local or general anaesthetic.

An operation before the fourteenth week of pregnancy may be carried out using a suction curette. The foetus is removed by a method known as aspiration. Alternatively, the neck of the womb is gently dilated and the contents scraped out in a procedure like a D & C (which stands for dilation and curretage). You can choose to stay in overnight but in many places this is just a day operation.

Termination of pregnancy by either of these methods is safe and there is very little danger of complication. If you have left it until after the fourteenth week of pregnancy, things are rather different. The foetus is now too large and well-formed to be simply sucked out. For this reason, abortion is carried out by injecting prostoglandins, which are hormones, into the uterus. This causes the uterus to contract and go into labour. The developing foetus has to be expelled vaginally, so the mother must go through much the same process as giving birth, except to a dead baby. This is a distressing and a painful procedure for the mother.

In the past, when abortion was not so readily available or was illegal at certain times, women have invariably resorted to other ways of dealing with unwanted pregnancies. The British Abortion Act of 1967 was introduced to protect women from 'backstreet' abortionists who frequently caused the death or sterility of women who had sought abortion by their lack of hygiene and the methods used.

The Catholic church condemns all induced abortion while the Protestant church has a more flexible approach. Islamic law allows abortion up to as late as 120 days; in Jewish law the foetus is always regarded as part of the mother and abortion is permitted as long as several doctors recommend it. Hindu teachings allow abortion only when the pregnancy is actually endangering the mother. If you come from a religious family, you may find yourself under pressure from other family members or from your preacher about which decision to take. But most people agree that the right to choose lies with the mother who will have to look after the child for the next eighteen years.

Whatever anyone tells you, a baby is very well attached inside of you. Jumping down stairs, horse riding, drinking gin and sitting in a hot bath, taking laxatives or stupidly inserting any foreign object into your vagina will not get rid of a baby – but may damage you for the rest of your life.

Over the last ten to fifteen years, the numbers of one parent families have risen considerably, the stigma of 'abandoned mother' no longer exists and so you should not feel compelled to have your child adopted or aborted just because you don't have a partner.

You may decide to carry your child full-term for various reasons. You might find that you cannot tolerate the idea of abortion because it is against your religion or beliefs, or for reasons of health or finance, or to do with your relationship with the father or your family. Alternatively, you may have ignored your pregnancy until it was too late to have an abortion performed. If you are not sure what decision to take, various societies exist, such as the National Council for One Parent Families, that will be able to advise you and will perhaps help you to make your decision.

If finally, you do decide to have your child adopted, you should register with your local doctor, informing him of your decision. He will be able to arrange ante-natal care for you and will organise a hospital bed. You should then contact your Local Welfare Office (part of your local Social Services Department) who will arrange the adoption for you (although there are also several voluntary adoption agencies). At the back of this book are lists of associations and advisory services who will outline the legal issues involved. (i.e. The Children's Act of 1975 gave an adopted person over the age of eighteen the right of access to his original birth records, to be given with access to counselling.)

You should also be aware that, if you do not want to care for your baby during the first six weeks before adoption, you must arrange for the baby to be fostered during that period, before the birth. Six weeks after the child is born you will be asked to sign a form of consent. Providing that the attending social worker is convinced that you are not under any pressure to make your decision, that will be all you are required to do.

Although adoption might seem a simple option, don't forget that you will have carried your child full-term and given birth – all of which can be a very emotional experience. You may find it even more distressing to have to relinquish your baby.

HAVING YOUR BABY

If you decide you are going to keep your baby, you are going to experience a full-term pregnancy. The doctor will be able to estimate the date that your baby is due to arrive by counting nine months from your last period and adding seven days. In truth, this is just an expected date of delivery, and delivery could be a week or two either side of it. First babies in particular have a tendency to be late.

Hopefully, your parents and your boyfriend will be supportive of your decision to go ahead and have the baby. The months before the birth of the child should be spent as much as possible not only enjoying your pregnancy now you have decided to carry on with it, but also making as many preparations for what's ahead of you as you possibly can.

It is impossible for any book or person who does not know you and your totally unique situation to advise you on all the different things you will need to know in the next few months. But there are people who will be qualified to advise you about continuing your school or work life, arranging housing problems, telling you about local crèches and other childcare facilities, if you plan to continue in your job. They will be able to counsel you about financial benefits available to you from the government and the everyday questions about your pregnancy and birth that you are bound to have.

Getting pregnant, as many girls have discovered to their chagrin, is no longer any guarantee of a proposal. Forty years ago shotgun weddings, as they were known, were a more common occurrence. But nowadays, luckily, few boys feel they can be tricked this way into a marriage that they don't want. On the other hand, if your relationship is fairly long-standing and maybe you were already even both thinking of marriage, your pregnancy might simply hurry things up. Now is the time for both of you to be thinking about what would make you happiest. Your baby, you will find, will be happiest when you are. But don't feel that you must get married just because you are pregnant – and don't let your parents try to persuade you that this is your only alternative. You may want to wait before you get married, or you may genuinely feel that the man who has made you pregnant is not the person you want to spend the rest of your life with.

One little note that is worth mentioning: while very few women who already have a baby can imagine their lives without that child, and will tell you of the happiness that the child has brought them, statistically very young mothers are also more likely to neglect and batter their children. Once you have your baby at home with you, it is important, particularly for the young mum, to try and develop a network of activities and alternatives. There are bound to be single parent groups, such as Gingerbread, in your area where you can meet other parents. There will also be nurseries and playgroups. The advantage of getting to know about all of these is two-fold: not only will you and your baby be getting out and about, which is good for both of you, but you will also meet parents who will be able to babysit for you – if you are happy to do the same for them occasionally. This alleviates the common problem of feeling trapped at home changing nappies while all your old friends are out having a good time. It is imperative that early on, you find a couple of people who would be happy to spend the odd evening with your baby, because you must remember that no young baby must *ever* be left alone, even for a few minutes while you pop out. You might feel that you are imposing on your mother if she lives nearby but, in truth, most grandmothers have been longing for the day when they can once again have a small child to pamper. Now is a good time to try to cement family relationships, particularly if you are not with the father of the baby. Grandparents, aunties and uncles all provide a network of help that will take a lot of the pressure off you if you ever have moments when you have to get away. Everyone sometimes feels that they would like a few minutes to themselves, and you will be no different and it is nothing to be ashamed of. On the other hand, it is a good idea to be prepared for these moments by having someone you can rely on to take over, however briefly.

Questions and answers

Q Does an abortion make you sterile?

A No. An abortion in itself cannot make you sterile, except if you get a major infection afterwards which is left untreated. This could affect your Fallopian tubes, but sterility after an abortion has become very unusual. After an abortion, a woman is usually advised to shower rather than bath for the first three days. It is also better to use sanitary towels rather than tampons for the first few days. In addition, clinics and hospitals usually advise women to have a medical check-up six weeks after an abortion. And if you are in any pain or have unusual bleeding, get in touch with your doctor before then.

Q What is a miscarriage?

A In a miscarriage, the expectant mother loses her baby against her wishes. About fifteen per cent of pregnancies end in miscarriages. These usually occur during the first three months, usually between the sixth and tenth week of the pregnancy, sometimes before the mother even knows she is having a baby. Three-quarters of all these miscarriages are caused by some fault in the foetus or by some defective implantation of the foetus inside the womb. Miscarriage can be extremely distressing, even if you weren't sure you wanted the baby. But it does not mean that you will not be able to carry another pregnancy full-term.

Q What is a therapeutic abortion?

A A therapeutic abortion is the deliberate termination of a pregnancy. According to the law in the UK, it can be carried out only after two doctors, one of whom must be a specialist in these things, have agreed that the mother or her children is threatened or that the foetus is handicapped.

Q Is it true you can't get pregnant during breastfeeding?

A No. This is an old wives' tale and is completely untrue. Your periods may very well return during breastfeeding, although sometimes breastfeeding delays their onset. In reality, as soon as you have given birth and before you have resumed your sex life, you must think about contraception. At least until you have recovered and adjusted again. One good thing is that you may find your doctor is willing to suggest additional alternative methods of contraception now that you have had a child, for instance, he might consider an IUD.

Q Can I have sex now that I am pregnant?

A Yes, if you wish. Pregnancy is often a time when you and your boyfriend will feel very loving and want to be as close as you can be. You will also have no worries about contraception for once! But you may find some positions are uncomfortable and it will take a little trial and error to find ones which accommodate your bump. You should also take care to be gentle. Some men don't want to make love because they are afraid that it may dislodge the baby, and also because they get odd ideas about doing something sexual when there is a baby present. One friend of mine has not made love with his girlfriend for the last four or five months of her pregnancy because he got the idea that the baby might bite his dick!

If there is a tendency to miscarry in the first three months, your doctor may advise you not to make love during this time. You must get advice from him. Medical opinion is also divided on whether it is wise to make love during the last month. My personal opinion is that, unless your doctor has told you not to, go ahead if you feel like it. You may even find that you feel even sexier than usual, because pregnancy has a way of bringing one very close to one's animal ancestors. It is not unheard of at the end of pregnancy for the contractions of orgasm to start your labour.

Q When I have my baby, will they cut me?

A The cut is called an episiotomy. This is performed by doctors or midwives to prevent tearing when the baby's head comes out. Some women are more worried about this than by any other aspect of giving birth. It is nothing to worry about. If you are bothered you should discuss it with your doctor beforehand. When you are actually having your baby, that is not the time to start discussing the way you want to do it. The cut is usually stitched up afterwards using dissolving stitches which don't need to be removed. Sometimes doctors will use ordinary stitches which will be removed by the midwife when she visits you at your home during the following two weeks after the birth. This is the time to mention if you have any unusual discomfort. Everyone hurts a bit for several days after having a baby, and lots of doctors will prescribe an analgesic. Some women worry that their stitches might come open when they make love. Your stitches will be long healed before you start making love again.

Q Can a girl get pregnant even if she hasn't started her periods?

A Yes. As soon as you have started to ovulate, you can become pregnant. Since you ovulate two weeks to ten days before your first period, if you have unprotected sex before that period would have arrived, it is still possible to be pregnant. So no girl should use the excuse that she hasn't started her periods as a reason for not getting contraception if she plans to make love.

Q My boyfriend is very upset because I am planning to have an abortion. What's it to do with him?

A Because unwanted pregnancy is a woman's problem physically, it is often her emotional problems that receive all the attention. Her friends, parents, doctor and maybe even a counsellor at the clinic should help her through this crisis. But this can be a very, very difficult time for men as well. And most men will find it hard to find the same emotional attention the woman is getting, especially as some people tend to regard it as his 'fault'. Although ideally the abortion decision is made jointly, in reality and in the eyes of the law, the decision is the woman's. No matter how much her boyfriend or even husband may want to keep his child – and it *is* his as much as hers – he may find himself powerless. You should try and support each other as much as you possibly can and you must always remember that this is a very painful time for him too. He may even need to seek professional counselling to enable him to talk about the problem, which your doctor can recommend. How you react to an abortion is a litmus test of instincts and emotions. It may signal the beginning or the end of a relationship. It is an obvious reaction to try to lay the blame for your pregnancy on your boyfriend. That is a way of absolving yourself from responsibility. But like it or not, you are both equally responsible for what has happened and if you try to make him feel bad, you will only end up feeling worse.

Q Is it possible to continue working after I have had my baby?

A Yes, depending on what you do. Obviously, if your job involves night shifts, you will find it very difficult to carry on working unless your partner is prepared to stay at home with the baby all night. Legally, your boss cannot sack you for getting pregnant, and if you have worked for the same employer for two years, you are entitled to full maternity leave and your job must be kept open for you on your return. Your local Citizens' Advice Bureau will tell you all about your rights and will be able to help if your employer does not comply with the law. Some employers try to put pressure on their employees not to come back to work afterwards because they feel that a new mother will not do her job with the same devotion as before.

No matter how strongly you feel before you give birth, you cannot quite predict what your attitude will be afterwards. Some women cannot bear to leave their babies at all, and other women do not feel complete if they have given up a promising career, and may start to resent the baby if they have to stay at home. So it is best to try to keep an open mind about it until you have spent a little time after the birth with your baby. It is true that more and more women now work after they have a child than ever before. However, these women are often plagued with guilt about leaving their young children with childminders or in crèches. These are all decisions you will have to make once you actually have the baby and you should give them long and careful thought.

You may feel that if you are financially able to, your easiest route to satisfaction is having a part-time job of some kind, or even developing a business from home, utilising a talent you may have not realised before. There are books on starting your own business from home in your public library – which is also, incidentally, a good place to find out about groups for young mothers and small children. If you decide to start your own business, you may even find you are eligible for a small business grant. Find out about this, again, at your Citizens' Advice Bureau.

Q I am pregnant and my parents have thrown me out. Who can I turn to?

A Your boyfriend and his parents may feel that they have some responsibility to you, particularly if you have had a reasonable rapport in the past. If so, this will at least tide you over until your parents have recovered from their shock and have got used to the idea. Now is not the time to be too proud to make it up with them if they extend any kind of peace offering. You may never forget that they threw you out when you needed them most, but they will probably equally always blame themselves for not having been supportive. You have to understand that discovering you are pregnant is as big a shock for them as it is for you and people often say things in the heat of the moment which they come to regret later.

If you are actually homeless, your local council is obliged to provide you with a roof over your head. It would be worth bearing in mind that even though your parents may be difficult to communicate with at this time, you may have other relations who will be surprisingly sympathetic. You may get more response from an older sister or brother, an aunt or uncle, or even your grandparents, simply because they are a little bit further removed from the problem but can still see both sides. Now is definitely not the time to pack your bags and head for the big city. You need your friends and your support system and you will feel lonelier and be more vulnerable in a place you don't know and where nobody knows you. Try and stay put and grin and bear it, perhaps staying with friends. Most parents do come round, if not before the birth then as soon as they've taken one look at the new baby – which is, after all, part of their family.

Q I come from a very strict religious family and I daren't tell my mother that I think I'm pregnant.

A At some point soon, unless you are going to have an abortion and feel that you can keep this secret from them – which may actually be very difficult to organise, as your parents probably want to know where you are most of the time – your mother will not need to be told; she will know. Mothers have an unfortunate sixth sense about these things, as you may find out in the next few weeks. You may think you've put on an Oscar-winning performance of calm, but she will see through it. It is also the first thing a mother thinks of at any sign of snivelling around the house. Your parents inevitably are going to be furious. Fathers, in particular, let alone fathers whose social standing can be affected by something like this, react angrily and maybe threaten things that your mother will not allow him to carry out. All you can do is sit tight and try and rebuild their confidence and trust in you. The good part in all this is that a problem shared really is a problem halved. You don't know how they're going to react until you tell them and in your mind you're turning it into something worse than any reality.

If the worst comes to the worst, and they do throw you out or try to banish you to some elderly relation even abroad, you are going to have to seek help elsewhere. Social workers are used to dealing with problems like this, that arise fairly regularly within certain religious or ethnic groups, so get in touch with your local Department of Health and Social Security. You may think, if they want to send you away, that you must go. But there is no law that can make you leave, unless you are under sixteen. If there is any chance of you getting married, this will probably alleviate the problem for your parents – but don't be forced into that either. This is your choice and you are going to have to live with it – and with the person you marry. Unless that person is the one you feel you want to be with, you are compounding one problem with another.

Q How does a pregnancy test work?

A A pregnancy test works by detecting the hormones that the growing placenta secretes. They can usually be done ten days after a missed period. It can also be done by a blood test but a urine test is much more common.

Q I had an abortion some time ago and I still cry all the time about it and become very upset if I see a little baby. Will this pass?

A The feelings of depression felt by women after a miscarriage or an abortion vary in intensity. At one end of the scale, some women go through a short period of feeling depressed and tearful for a couple of weeks afterwards, in part caused by their hormone levels reverting to normal after the boosted levels during pregnancy. But sometimes a more serious depression can develop because you may feel that you can't get your problem out into the open. You may be blaming yourself, feeling that you have failed in some way or simply wondering what would have happened if you had gone through with the pregnancy.

You need to talk to somebody about this – your Family Planning clinic is used to dealing with upset girls and will be able to refer you to a counsellor specialising in helping girls at this difficult time. You may never quite get over a traumatic event like the loss of a baby, nor should you expect to, but the depression will fade.

8 *Wanking is bad for you and other myths*

'It was at the end of my freshman year of high school – and freshman year of masturbating – that I discovered on the underside of my penis, just where the shaft meets the head, a little discolored dot that has since been diagnosed as a freckle. Cancer. I had given myself cancer. All that pulling and tugging at my own flesh, all that friction, had given me an incurable disease. And not yet fourteen! In bed at night the tears rolled from my eyes. "No!" I sobbed. "I don't want to die! Please – no!" But then, because I would very shortly be a corpse anyway, I went ahead as usual and jerked off into my sock.'

Whacking Off from PORTNOY'S COMPLAINT
by Philip Roth

If you were to ask a roomful of people if they wanked regularly, a couple of men would probably admit that they did. Lots of the girls would probably go rather red and mumble things like, 'Don't ask stupid questions.' Wanking is one of those sexual topics that has a million and one myths attached to it, simply because people don't want to admit that they enjoy doing it. You can hardly imagine the romantic hero of a movie coming into a love scene saying, 'Hey, baby, I had a really good wank last night, it was great, yeah.' Wanking, just by the very way it sounds, somehow doesn't have that certain something. Even worse is the word masturbating, which really does sound like something they do in the sluice room on *General Hospital*. In fact, they may well do it in the sluice room on *General Hospital* . . .

So, having accepted that nobody admits to it and everyone does it, here are a few of the other myths – you won't go blind or deaf, no part of your anatomy will drop off, it won't ruin your future sex life, it won't make hairs grow on the palms of your hands, it's not dirty, it won't turn you into a nymphomaniac – in fact, it's more likely to put you to sleep. You may worry that you would like to wank fifteen times a day. This is nothing to worry about. It may be difficult, however, to find the time in which to do it. It is perfectly normal to want to do something that feels good as often as possible. It's rather like having a chocolate – once you've had one, you might as well finish the box off.

Myths

There are many myths about sex. Most sixteen-year-olds spend huge amounts of time passing on pieces of information to each other in whispered tones that are in fact completely and utterly incorrect. What's even worse is that what may have started out only a little bit inaccurate can end up like a game of Chinese Whispers. You started off by saying that Prince is a good dancer and by the time it reaches the Upper Sixth common room it ends up that Prince was in the playground at break drinking milk out of some girl's navel.

A lot of our sexual myths and the way we imagine romance ought to be comes from watching films, reading books and those really dumb girlie magazines. It's from all of this that we often contrive our expectations. We see romance in terms of extremely slim couples holding hands on the beach walking into the sunset, playing snowballs, running in slow motion across a cornfield – although anyone who has tried running in slow motion will find it is almost a physical impossibility. Girls also imagine that boys are going to be strong, dark and handsome. And boys in turn are equally tempted to visualise their perfect girl as a Barbie doll who can cook. While these myths are perfectly harmless and disappear as soon as you meet a real boyfriend or girlfriend and can stop living in a fantasy of what it might be like and enjoy reality instead, there are some myths which can remain with you for a long time and aren't that great to live with.

1 Alcohol is good for sex: All alcohol is a depressant. It lowers reaction times, numbs sensations and in large quantities will make you puke or pass out, neither of which are high on the list of attractive things to do in front of men or women. In small doses, a drink or two may help to relax you and does tend to lower your inhibitions. On the other hand, you may discover that all it takes is a little wine to make you regurgitate your last three meals in the back of his Cortina. Also, in large doses it is the single most common cause of men losing their hard-ons, or not getting one in the first place.

121

2 Men do all the work: There is this eternal vision in women's minds of the night that the great romance climaxes and it almost always follows a scenario where he sweeps you off your feet, up a winding staircase and throws you on the leopard-skin rug upstairs in front of a roaring log fire. Meanwhile, in this great symphony of romance, the woman is a passive instrument whispering 'Take me, take me' and whimpering alluringly as she gets a leopard claw jabbed in her backside.

The advantage of imagining that men do all the work means that everything is left up to him as to when it happens and how it happens – which in some cases may be a responsibility you don't wish to take. However, a totally non-aggressive role has its disadvantages. You may feel completely out of control of the situation, and you may, by just following the flow, deny yourself the opportunity to do things *you* want to do. The ideal is a relationship which is an equal partnership, however rare this is. It's all very well acting the doormat sometimes for fun, but you may well find yourself having to live this role. And nobody wants to live their life with WELCOME stamped on their chest.

3 Sex 'just happens': Sex isn't something that suddenly looms up in the middle of the cinema apropos nothing, in fact. Even if your boyfriend isn't Mr Foreplay, there is almost always some build-up to the actual act. Therefore to behave as though sex is some kind of huge shock, like somebody jumping out from behind a door and saying boo at you, is not being entirely honest with yourself. It is also not being entirely honest with oneself if you are going out regularly with a girl or boy to say that sex has never crossed your mind. Almost everyone, when they are going out with someone and they have got over the initial stages of getting to know each other, thinks about sex a good part of the time. They also make decisions in their own minds far in advance of the actual moment when it happens as to whether or not they're going to say yes or no. Some people do get carried away by the strength of their feelings at the time. If you feel it is likely that you are going to put yourself into a situation where things can get seriously out of hand (or in hand, as the case may be), then you are very foolish indeed not to be prepared for what might happen. Adolescent sexual urges are incredibly strong.

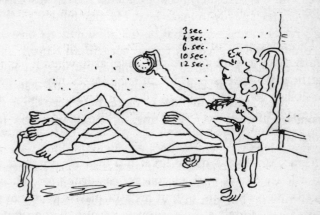

While it's true that sexual feelings are natural, lovemaking expertise has to be learned. Everyone knows instinctively what to do but they don't necessarily know how to do it very well. While there are those who would compare us immediately with animals, it should be remembered that higher animals like monkeys learn to do it by watching, which is something we rarely have the opportunity to do. The myth that lovemaking comes naturally to people also implies that it is somehow very unromantic not to know what to do or to be able to show your partner how to do something in a way which pleases. Teaching each other brings intimacy into a relationship.

4 Everyone's erogenous zones are the same: They are, more or less. However, many lovers tend to see each other in terms of set areas that they should grope at in order to get a response while the rest of the body remains a sort of murky no man's land. Pleasure is where you find it and, with somebody you particularly like, you may be amazed at the areas that suddenly become very sensitive. It is always a mistake to imagine that everyone is alike. If in doubt, ask.

5 A man can always tell when a woman is ready to make love: There is absolutely no way for a man to tell absolutely if a woman feels ready to make love. He may think it feels like she's ready to make love, but he might be entirely mistaken. According to the noted sex researcher, Alfred Kinsey, about half of couples have three to ten minutes of foreplay before intercourse. Recent clinical evidence suggests that many women need fourteen minutes or more. Boys need about four seconds and may even find that brushing past you in a doorway is enough.

6 Men can always make love: If a man is very tired, has had a lousy day at work or college, has drunk too much or rowed with his parents, or hurt his back playing rugby, or just doesn't feel entirely at ease with you, it may all contribute to him either not wanting to make love or not being able to. In this situation it is not the absence of his hard-on which may worry him, it is the humiliation he may feel as a result. Even if you are understanding and don't cry or fall off the bed laughing, his lack of erection may make him feel he has not lived up to the myth that he should be able to have sex at any time, in any place, at any moment. In fact, if he could stop worrying about his hard-on, and focus on the other sensations he may be finding pleasurable, his willie may assert its own will.

Not getting a hard-on, a.k.a. impotence, can be a vicious circle. He may worry so much about not getting it up once that the next time you get into bed, he's so terrified it will happen again that it does; and so on. So you have to be very understanding and it might be best to concentrate on non-sexual pursuits for a while so as not to put him under any undue pressure.

7 Big tits are best/big knobs are best: The fashions in breast size change almost with the decade, or sometimes even more often. In the twenties it was important to be entirely flat-chested and people used to bind them with elastic bandages to achieve a boyish look. In the fifties it was fashionable to have enormous bazongas shaped like ice-cream cones, and women wore circle-stitched conical bras to achieve that intriguing look. But it is important, fashion apart, to try and think of your tits as not being some kind of anatomical accessory. They are not sexy or unsexy, they are a part of you. The problem often is that you want what you haven't got; girls with big bosoms often stand with their shoulders almost touching at the front and their arms crossed, and dream of having a slim, boyish figure. Girls with slim, boyish figures yearn for undulating curves. As for men, breast size is just simply a matter of personal taste. Some like big ones, some like small ones and most don't care either way, it's the girl they are attached to which matters.

All of the above applies also to knob size.

8 Too much wanking spoils your sex life: According to theories, the real truth of this matter is that the more a woman has masturbated herself, the more likely she is to have an orgasm during foreplay or intercourse for three reasons. One, she will know what pleases her, and two, she can do it herself while they're doing it, and three, she feels more at home with her own body and its reactions.

9 There is a right and wrong way for a woman to have an orgasm: Sigmund Freud is behind this particular myth because he created a supposed difference between the clitoral orgasm (the 'bad' one) and vaginal orgasm (the 'good' one) – which is of course a load of old bollocks. An orgasm is a response all over your body and there is no such thing as a vaginal orgasm, since all orgasm requires some pressure on the clitoris, which may be achieved through the action of intercourse. The clitoris is the centre of sexual excitement for women. Unfortunately it is not very well-positioned for actual intercourse since it is outside the vagina. It may get subjected to a certain amount of stimulation indirectly but it is well clear of the real action going on.

In the early sixties, Masters & Johnson conducted a famous sex survey. During this they measured the physical intensity of female orgasms. They discovered that the strongest orgasms were on average experienced through masturbation. The second most intense orgasm was through manual or oral stimulation by a partner. The least intense orgasm was through intercourse. Kinsey found that most men (75%) have an orgasm within two minutes after penetration. And most women (75%) need more than two minutes of stimulation to achieve orgasm. According to recent findings, many women need fourteen minutes of stimulation, so this leaves a twelve minute gap between the male and female orgasm. Which leads us neatly on to (. . .)

10 Simultaneous orgasms are the best kind: Often, people imagine that they have come together when in fact it wasn't even close, nor does it need to have been. When you consider the differences in timing between most men and women's lovemaking, however in tune they may be with each other, you have to ask yourself, is it really the romantic ideal it's cracked up to be. Also, if you have your orgasms at different times you are then more able to enjoy your partner's orgasm separately.

11 Contraception is a woman's responsibility: Although this should be a myth, it is often true – though in an ideal world it wouldn't be. In an ideal world, men would ask 'Do you have contraception?' and beforehand rather than in the rosy afterglow. Thus, it should be a myth but it isn't and any girl who relies on her boyfriend to be responsible, unless she has known him for a very long time and their relationship is very strong, is making a big mistake.

12 Men lose interest in girls after they have made love: This has two different applications. The first one is when a man and woman have just made love and she wants to sit in bed reminiscing about their first meeting, how both of them felt, what they were wearing, what they'd just eaten, what he said to her, what she said to him and what happened next. He, on the other hand, has pulled the duvet over his head and is snoring soundly. What she probably doesn't realise is that this is simply because after coming, a man's excitement stops sharply and gives way to exhaustion. He is sleeping not because he is insensitive, uncaring, a beast and a pig, but because he's tired out.

The second application of this is women who are worried that the man with whom they are contemplating starting a sexual relationship, will leave them the minute he's shagged them and not want to go on any more dates. If this thought has crossed your mind, then it is probably wise to wait a great deal longer before sleeping with this man, particularly if he has a reputation for doing so. It is playing with fire, however attractive boys with bad reputations inevitably are. Every girl likes to think she can tame a Lothario. Many girls know to their cost that this is not true and that boys with a history of sleeping around are likely to go on doing so for some time.

9 *Angst, angst and yet more angst*

What is normal?

As it is almost impossible for me to tell you what is normal, what I am simply going to do in this chapter is describe some of the things that some people like to do but which may worry them because they aren't strictly what everyone else does.

Crushes

The teenage years are well known as being a time when many of us develop crushes on members of our own sex. I once had a crush on a boy from North London. He had a thick neck, a square jaw and he looked so healthy that it was a bit like associating with a Communist inspirational statue. He had an accent which my granny would have said sounded like 'a bit of the rough'. This, of course, made him even more desirable.

When finally our lips met (in the back of a taxi) I developed lockjaw from the shock of it all. So when our lips parted, I let out a yelp like a parrot shot by a suppository. I also nearly knocked myself unconscious getting out of the taxi and rounded off the whole display of *savoir faire* by tripping over my own foot. Unlike my plan, I behaved more like Barbara Woodhouse than Scarlett O'Hara setting out on the rampage. And that, to put it mildly, was the end of that. I still shudder at the memory.

Contrary to popular belief, a crush is not something that only happens to teenage girls in convents. Nor do they always centre on the PE mistress. I can't imagine anything worse than

developing a 'pash', as we called them at school, on a brisk, firm and jolly woman in a tracksuit with a whistle round her neck. But most of us have endured a crush of sorts at some point. Men are susceptible too, which no-one ever seems to mention. So are very good-looking people, perhaps because that side of their lives tends to be fairly easy, so it makes a change for them to meet someone who shows as much interest as the North Face of the Eiger.

Having a crush should be treated as one of life's lighter moments. It reminds you that, despite thinking you're the

130

second Simone Signoret, underneath you're still able to be quite a prat. You suddenly start blushing, tripping and generally being a twerp of the first order. You notice that if you actually talk to the crushee in question everything you say is complete and utterly baloney – and all of it squeaked out in a high-pitched voice that hasn't been heard since the days of Caruso on seventy-eight r.p.m. records. Adding to the distress you feel is the fact that the more conscious you become of your voice, the shriller it gets.

These are possibly the reasons that crushes are usually directed towards unobtainable people. Pop stars, doctors, teachers and the local vicar are all excellent candidates for six frenzied weeks – of absolutely nothing happening. Which is what happens during crushes. Men think you're too cool by half and are therefore unlikely to fling themselves at you unless they've had one too many shandies down the disco. But the good thing about this is that you don't give too much of yourself away, and are less likely to feel a fool afterwards. (A young man told me that after one too many shandies down the disco.)

Crushes tend to go off rather rapidly. They're so fragile that the least hint of reality ruins them. It's best not to see the object of one's affections too often. A fleeting glimpse of his left ear once a week as he gets into his car (seen preferably through the binoculars) should be quite enough for anyone. Everyone I spoke to agreed that nothing cools the ardour quicker than seeing him/her eat. Seeing one's crushee stuffing their face with a Wimpy or a Big Whopper is not the kind of *Gone With The Wind* romance one yearns for. Also, anything to do with socks (like taking them off and flinging them at the laundry basket, or worse still, keeping them on) is an anathema to the crush.

Despite knowing all these things, devotees of the crushee will go to great lengths to see the poor unsuspecting punter on whom they have this fixation – like 'just passing Balham',

Nobody is ever just passing Balham – unless they're off on a polar expedition. Or, suggesting everyone at the party plays sardines when you've got raging claustrophobia. The list of weedy excuses is almost endless.

A friend of mine given to this condition regularly ruins her wild passions by actually doing something about them. This is fatal. She had a crush on one of the clerks in the local bank, which resulted in her taking out fifteen un- needed loans. Then it all came to an abrupt halt when he took her for a drink and earnestly told her his hobby was banger racing. No-one can have fantasies about an Adonis bank clerk who goes banger racing. She then went on to have a crush on this terrible lout who looked a bit like Alain Delon on a bad night. One evening he showed up at her flat and nonchalantly asked if she'd like to take his trousers off. I was very impressed when I heard this. Here was a boy who really believed in the direct approach. He then dragged her all over the purple swirling Wilton carpet, which gave her a burn mark down her behind. She immediately rang to tell me the episode had got him totally out of her system, and he was never heard of again.

Crushes make you constantly aware of how silly you are being, but perhaps this is one of the nicer aspects. You feel like a thirteen-year-old, which isn't all bad. Crushes feel like the first few months of being madly in love, except that the semi-hysterical, apprehensive feeling stays because the lovely cosy feeling never arrives. Although you'll be rushing off to the tanning parlour, cocoa butter in your sweaty mitt, and parading about in mini skirts that get you arrested, you'll never get to enjoy lolling in bed with your frozen feet between his thighs and a jolly good Agatha Christie. That may sound less than riveting, but it's the stuff that love affairs, not crushes, are based on. If it's a crush, come three a.m. you'll be watching the dawn rise over his skylight or perching nervously on his bedside table doing raffia work for light relief.

In the long run, it's best to find someone who won't spoil everything by opening his mouth and saying, 'Oi mate, 'ow 'bout a quick one?' when you'd been planning to act out the farewells from *Anna Karenina* down at Paddington. And some crushes should be kept strictly to oneself. Not that they're ever exactly Pentagon state secrets. On the other hand, girlfriends will be kept endlessly amused by the constant stream of non-events. Sadly, most of their experiences pale now I've heard about the Wilton carpet episode. Even if you try to keep quiet, people suffering a crush tend to look as if they've had a dose of strychnine whenever the object of their passion is within a ten mile radius. This makes you look an even bigger twit, but you have been warned. Some crushes, of course, do develop into great love affairs. Lady Caroline Lamb had a whopper on Byron, but she blew it. She was more than a trifle over the top. Then again, any man who supposedly lived off vinegar and boiled potatoes to keep his body slim and his complexion pale, can't be trusted with one's deepest feelings.

It would be unfair to write crushes off as mere frivolity. It's also wrong to confuse them with obsessions, which give you even worse hot flushes. Very occasionally, what starts as a mad crush develops into love. No mean feat if you can't face food for the first three months of it all.

Years ago, I had deep longings for a man, mainly because of his long legs. One night, in the middle of dinner, I decided I had to fly there and then to Paris to see him. Upon arrival, I teetered off into the dark night in search of the object of my crush, a filthy French taxi driver in tow. The situation was made worse by the fact that the only two words of French I knew were *oui* and *courgette*. Neither of these came up in my conversation with the cabbie. Finally, I located my true love. I looked like I'd just arrived from the Crimea and had frostbite in all the places worth seeing, plus I hadn't had my tea so I was tetchy as well. So why do I approve of the impetuosity of crushes so much? Quite simply because I fell so much in love with that one . . .

Sometimes, however, these crushes may be intense and passionate feelings which worry us, although they are rarely consummated physically. They shouldn't be confused with homosexuality but seen as a perfectly normal stage of growing up. Some teenagers, though, do form homosexual attachments which are either a phase, or may prove to be a permanent part of their sexuality.

Homo/hetero

This raises two problems. The first one is that it is illegal for boys under twenty-one to indulge in homosexual activity. This law came into being in Queen Victoria's time. It is not illegal for young women, and this is because Queen Victoria quite simply refused to believe that young women could possibly do such things to each other.

The second problem is often one's parents. It is hard initially for the young homosexual to decide whether or not to 'come out' and be open about their decision, and it is unwise to limit yourself too soon by announcing it to your parents. A teenager may feel very apprehensive about his or her parents' reaction, and could easily be terrified that they will want to either disown them, or ask them to seek 'treatment' as though it is an illness.

Human sexual behaviour is very varied. Nowadays, no one way is considered to be 'the right way', and sexual variations are only limited by the partner's individual drives and pre-ferences. In Western society today, heterosexuality is the norm, but, in the last thirty years, huge steps have been made by the homosexual community to be accepted.

What do homosexuals do? For girls, this usually involves kissing and petting, stroking each other's breasts and genitals and oral sex. For homosexual men, besides actual anal inter-

134

course – which not all homosexual couples indulge in, and is illegal even between consenting adults (anyone) in this country – activities include kissing, stroking, mutual wanking and oral sex.

A recent and worrying development, primarily at this stage for the homosexual community, has been AIDS, or Acquired Immune Deficiency Syndrome. AIDS was first described in America, in 1980. People most likely to contract this illness are drug addicts (through the sharing of dirty hypodermic needles) and homosexuals, although it is gradually being introduced into the heterosexual community as members of both those groups pass it on during sexual intercourse of any kind. At one point there was also a danger of contracting AIDS if you had to have a blood transfusion but now all blood is screened before it is administered. There was never, and never will be, any danger of catching AIDS by giving blood.

What the spread of AIDS means, for homosexuals in particular, is that there is now a campaign for 'Safe Sex', which means no exchange of body fluids. Many homosexuals are now using Durex, although these are not thought to be 100% protection. To be absolutely on the safe side, stick to hugging, rubbing and mutual masturbation. AIDS is also discussed in Chapter Ten.

Suspecting that you have homosexual tendencies, whether you are a boy or a girl, is likely to be an emotional crisis. You may feel very lonely, as if nobody else understands, you may worry that your 'straight' friends will turn away from you, you may be upset by the idea that if you are gay you may never be able to marry and have a family life. Many gays are as capable as heterosexual couples of enjoying a long-term, deep relationship with someone they love. The best thing to do is to talk to someone about your feelings, and there are several groups which provide emotional support and advice for gays, by gays. The addresses are at the back of the book.

Bisexuality

If someone is bisexual, this often means that he or she prefers their own sex but also enjoys sleeping with a member of the opposite sex as well. It is a problem to go out with somebody who is bisexual because when you go into a party, you not only have to worry about them fancying half the people there, you may have to worry about the entire crowd. It is very common for teenagers to indulge in some form of sexual contact with a member of their own sex. This does not mean you will necessarily remain bisexual: it is a phase of experimentation that many people go through on the path to discovering their own sexuality.

Oral sex

Also known as blow jobs, going down on someone or giving head. You cannot get pregnant from oral sex, but it does often lead to Other Things. Oral sex is putting your mouth on somebody else's rude bits. You then kiss and lick and caress those bits. Keen as I am to educate you in all things, I am absolutely *not* going to tell you how to do it. Suffice it to say that teeth are very unpopular. Your girlfriend or boyfriend and you will have to experiment to find out what feels best. Most men and women enjoy receiving oral sex enormously. But they may be tentative at first about giving it, partially because they may be unsure about exactly what to do and don't want to appear silly. And also because aesthetically, they may find it all a little overpowering at first. Oral sex, like many sexual matters, is something that should happen spontaneously. There is nothing worse than somebody suddenly shoving your head down the bed.

Women, particularly, sometimes worry that oral sex is an unnatural perversion. But in fact, it is a perfectly normal part of most people's lovemaking. It is perfectly safe. You cannot get pregnant from swallowing sperm, if you do choose to swallow it. If you decide not to, bear in mind that it is a little insensitive to spit it out on the candlewick bedspread immediately afterwards.

Anal sex

Anal sex is illegal for anyone in Britain and in many states in America. However, it is unusual to hear of couples dashing to the local cop shop to report this crime. The dangers of anal sex, apart from the homosexual risks outlined earlier, are that bacteria which are perfectly harmless in your bum can easily be transferred into the vagina and set off all manner of troublesome infections. There is also a risk of tearing, and piles for women who regularly indulge in it. It can also be excruciatingly painful.

Having said this, in case you are still wondering, anal sex consists of the man putting a well-lubricated willie up your bum.

Group sex

Group sex is more than two people having sex at the same time in the same place. Group sex enjoyed great popularity in the 1960s and is still rife in suburbia, where one famous variation has couples meeting at one house, throwing their car keys on the stripped pine coffee table and picking out another set of keys. You then go home with whoever the keys belong to. Smart 'swingers' go for the BMW key ring rather than the bike padlock. However, there seems to have been a decline in the popularity of group sex among young people. Quantity does not necessarily equate with quality.

Nymphomania

Most psychiatrists now agree that there is no such thing as a nymphomaniac, or a woman who 'can't get enough' and needs to shag constantly. However, some women may feel deprived of love at home, or in some way so insecure about themselves that the only way they can convince themselves of their own value and attraction is by seeking numerous different partners. Sadly, this is a vicious circle, as the more promiscuous they become, the less lovable and the more used they often feel. A woman who simply enjoys sex enormously is not a nymphomaniac, and some women do indeed have very strong sex drives. Boys are frequently quoted as saying that their ideal partner would be a dumb nymphomaniac who lived over a pub. (That was a joke, honest.)

Sex aids

There can be few things more disconcerting than lying in bed while some tall dark handsome man advances across the room with a fluorescent lime green willie. Apart from the fact that it might look as if he was about to serve you with a giant *enchilada*, what on earth do people say to each other in these situations? Even worse, what must it look like afterwards? A lizard's tail that just got caught in a swing door?

Whatever you might think of them, sex aids are big business. You only have to stroll through Soho to realise that. Nearly every shop in the area is crammed with equipment that would shame NASA, and posters on display showing nubile women nuzzling nonchalantly on fifteen-inch cucumbers or being knocked flat on their backs by tidal waves/fireworks/lorry drivers. After a week of practising going in and out of the back door with a paper bag over my head, I finally made it into my local sex shop. Here's a basic run-down:

1 The sprays to make your wanger bigger are, according to a friend who's tested several, rather like Vick's chest rub. His theory was, quite simply, that if you were convinced that it was going to move mountains then it might possibly work –

mind over matter. Also, the amount of rubbing involved to make any of it sink in is enough to get anyone going. The rubs/lotions all have a distinct resemblance to Copydex glue, which made me wonder if you were actually meant to glue your erection in place. For some obscure reason all of these lotions have racecourse connotations; they're called 'Stud' or 'Stally-on' so you only have to read the packet to feel as if you've spent the night with Red Rum.

All the gadgets for men's wangers look like terrible tortures. They range from see-through suction pipes with a bulb at the end to hanging weights. (Thinking about sex aids can make one quite philosophical. What is the meaning of life when there are men walking around their homes in Surbiton with pendulums strapped to their willies?)

2 The bust creams are a right load of cobblers – you might as well cover yourself in mayonnaise. There are even objects that you're supposed to lower your long-suffering bosom into, whereupon it is pelted with icy water. All this is more likely to make your chest retreat even further, rather than sally forth like Jayne Mansfield's.

3 In Japan it is fashionable for restaurants to advertise the food they serve by means of large plastic replicas in the window. All the vibrators I saw looked like blanched cucumbers or beached sea slugs. Even if I could sympathise with young men covering themselves with 'Hotstuff 6' ('makes a girl want to screw like a bunny'), I was quite baffled by the thought of all those women harbouring a vibrator in their knicker drawer. Worst of all were the ones with the little wiggly thing on them and the dreadful racket they make is rather disconcerting – like a doodlebug hit the duvet. With some of them, it must be rather similar to learning to drive, as they appear to go at about fifteen different speeds, depending on the mood you're in or whether you've got an appointment to keep. I didn't ask whether the wiggly thing went at the same speed – or even in the same direction.

4 And so we move rapidly on to male contraceptives: First there are the multi-coloured ones. Why, why, why, I ask myself, would anyone want to have a lilac Lovegun (as they are frequently referred to on the wrappers)? Then there are 'Union Jack' condoms and 'Hotrod' ticklers, complete with prongs, knobs and bumps on the ends. 'Will make her shriek,' said one packet, fairly accurately. Most of these bumpy ones come in a petunia-pink heavy plastic which looks as if they've been chopping up rubber gloves back at the factory and sending the fingers off to sex shops. I should imagine they take about three hours to get on and then you're in danger of cutting off your circulation (not to mention your . . .!) In fact, I think with sex aids the main aim is to get rigor mortis in as many places as possible.

5 The sexy movies are sold at the back of the shops with magazines like *Truss Monthly*. I was amazed at the increasing popularity of – wait for it – enemas! One shop had no fewer than twenty-three enema movies – maybe you got the hot-water bottles free with every purchase! The various plots ran along the lines of 'Debbie, wearing virgin white, is caught, severely chastised and then given an enema.' One thing I would love to know is, when the fans of this kind of activity are actually doing it, how they get the conversation around to giving you an enema. Are they nuzzling your neck one minute, and then pursuing you with a heated hose-pipe the next?

6 Finally, we mustn't forget all the little bits and pieces like 'Fire Red Pills' which you're supposed to slip into people's drinks to make them immediately rampant and raring to go. Or 'Ramrod' tablets that you can put into their food for a similar effect. And then there are all manner of knickers with holes in them, bras with holes in them, and every conceivable article of clothing with a hole in.

People have probably been rubbing 'Sta-Stiff Lotion' on

themselves since time immemorial. But these days, how do you keep from getting the giggles?

Questions and answers

Q   I want my boyfriend to give me oral sex. How can I suggest this to him and will he think it's dirty?

A   Try to find a way of showing him rather than actually telling him. For example, many men, if you are doing it to them, will do it to you. Try positioning yourself so that it seems a natural progression of your lovemaking. It might be a bit of a shock if you actually sit on his face but there are more subtle ways of manoeuvring yourself around the duvet. Most boys are a little apprehensive at first, but most of them then do like it. And don't worry about feeling dirty. As long as you are clean, he will like your smell as it is very much a part of your sexuality. The smell of a girl is much more sexy than the smell of a begonia.

Q   My boyfriend constantly looks at girlie magazines and has Page Three Girls plastered all over the inside of his desk. It makes me feel very unattractive and I have started to compare myself to them and wonder why he's going out with me.

A   He is probably going out with you because Samantha Fox wouldn't be interested, but I realise that this is not the consolation you are looking for. Most boys look at girlie magazines, partly because all their friends do and partly because they really like them. Some girls enjoy these magazines too. They are nothing to worry about. Just because he likes looking at a pretty girl with her legs in the air and no clothes on, doesn't mean he doesn't like the way you look as well. You may like looking at posters of John Taylor but it doesn't mean that every time you're with your boyfriend you are wishing he would metamorphose into JT at the bus stop. What you have to realise is that you are a real person and his real girlfriend and they are fantasies.

Q I am in love with my best friend. I would like to kiss her. If I see her talking to other girls at school I get really jealous. Should I confess to my friend that I am in love with her?

A I would definitely not confess to her that you are in love with her as this is likely to confuse and worry her. It is very normal for girls to have crushes on their best friends. It is because you are so close and see each other all the time and can relax together. It is very unusual for it to develop into a full-scale sexual relationship, although sometimes there is a bit of experimentation if both of you feel the same way. But unless she shows definite interest, content yourself with your friendship. As for you getting jealous, remember that if you become very possessive that will drive her further away.

Q My boyfriend wants me to wear stockings and suspenders. What on earth for?

A Men are attracted to various erogenous zones. The theory is that they like big bosoms to show that women will be able to feed their babies, small waists because this means they are not already pregnant and big hips which means they will have less problems giving birth. Men are also attracted to women's bottoms and their legs. This is probably because they are so very different from men's bottoms and legs and one tends to be attracted to the very things that are opposite in the opposite sex. Things like shortie nighties, and stockings and suspenders are really just icing on the cake. For example, with stockings and suspenders they are often worn with high heels which exaggerate the whole shape of the woman's body. And many men find them incredibly sexy, which is why they are still so popular when they are so impractical. Wanting you to wear something that he finds sexy is in no way odd or perverted unless you feel very uncomfortable pleasing him in this way.

Q Last week in the showers at the gym, another boy made a pass at me. I turned him down but have been thinking about it ever since. Does this mean I am gay and what should I do?

A When anything unusual happens in your life, there is a tendency to think about it for some time afterwards. For example, if a Martian had landed in the school changing-rooms, you would still be thinking about that, but it doesn't mean you automatically want to become a Martian. What happened to you may have felt quite strange and shocking at the time. You may even have felt some response, but you didn't do anything about it so I wouldn't worry too much. If he does it again, you should say clearly that you are not really interested. This will probably put him off.

   If you find that you do want to experiment – and many boys do at some time – then you will have to analyse your feelings once more. But one homosexual experience doesn't mean that you're going to be homosexual for the rest of your life and there's no point being guilty about it.

Q My boyfriend and I enjoy anal intercourse occasionally. Could it damage me?

A It could damage you if your boyfriend is not being gentle and using plenty of lubrication. He could rip you, or you could eventually get piles which are not the joke most people think they are. You could also get an infection if his

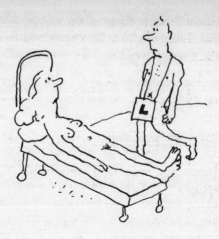

willie, having been up your bum, gets anywhere near your vagina. Infections can be easily transmitted, particularly yeast infections. So be wary.

Q My boyfriend likes me to wear my school uniform when we go out together and even sometimes to keep it on when we are in bed. I hate it. What should I do?

A If it bothers you, don't wear it. Or suggest he wears his and see how he likes that.

Q What should I do if my boyfriend suggests something that I really don't want to do. I don't want to lose him.

A You are unlikely to lose your boyfriend just because you are not willing to do something he would like you to. No girl or boy should submit to emotional blackmail and do something that they don't feel entirely happy doing. Half the point about sex is feeling relaxed and safe while you're doing it. Personally I would draw the line at anything involving family pets.

Q My girlfriend likes me to have oral sex with her but I have tried it and I really don't like the taste. How can I tell her without hurting her feelings.

A Have you tried smearing honey or peanut butter on her twat? Try it and if you really don't feel you are able to do something for your girlfriend which obviously she enjoys, you will have to find a way of telling her without implying that she is smelly or dirty. It could be a big blow to her confidence so be sensitive. And although your aversion does not mean that you are abnormal, you must make sure that she doesn't interpret your refusal as any indication that *she* is abnormal in wanting oral sex.

Q My boyfriend says if he puts a ground-up beetle on my dinner I will feel sexy. He says it is an aphrodisiac. What does that mean?

A An aphrodisiac is a food or substance that is meant to make you feel sexier. Some of the things that people have in the past regarded as aphrodisiacs include oysters, which are rather like eating snot in a soap dish, watercress, ground-up rhino horn (which he is unlikely to get hold of in Chorlton-cum-Hardy), and Spanish Fly, which is the ground-up beetle he mentioned to you and is in reality, extremely dangerous, as it irritates the linings of various sensitive organs inside your body. However, it is very difficult to get hold of the real thing and what he is probably talking about is something he has seen advertised in the back of a girlie magazine. It is a common delusion that alcohol and drugs have an aphrodisiac effect. In fact they impair your enjoyment and performance. Alcohol and drugs are very much to be avoided as either can result in you doing things you would never have considered or felt happy with had you been stone cold sober. And that leads to big regrets and recriminations, not to mention a great big hangover.

Q I came home early the other day to find my brother dressed in my clothes. Is there something wrong with him?

A A bit. Dressing up in women's clothing is called transvestism, and a man who dresses up in women's clothing is known as a transvestite. It is not dangerous, nor are they necessarily homosexual. When they dress up in clothing of the opposite sex, they feel an intense release of anxiety. It doesn't need to spoil his normal sex life but keeping this desire secret may be a strain. He will need a very understanding partner if he continues to want to dress up in women's clothes.

Q How many times a day is normal?

A Leonardo da Vinci and Isaac Newton are both reputed to have enjoyed sex up to ten times a day. This is unusual but not abnormal. It is very hard for anyone to say what is abnormal. The amount of times per day that a couple have sex depends entirely on their own desires. Sometimes once a week may be normal, and for others twice a day. For girls, the desire may fluctuate depending on the time of the month – she may feel very sexy before and during her period but not so sexy afterwards. It is important to understand that if your partner is not in the mood, it is probably nothing that you have done or failed to do. Sexual desire just fluctuates.

Q Is a love bite dangerous?

A A love bite is a revolting bruise often on the neck or chest, caused by sucking the skin up between your teeth. Teenagers particularly wear them as a kind of badge of sexual experience, i.e. 'Look, someone's been kissing me.' They also frequently go to great lengths to hide them from their parents and one of the most dangerous things about a love bite is the smack on the back of the head your mother will give you if she sees it. Band Aid and scarves are dead giveaways. Very few girls cut themselves on the neck or wear woolly scarves on sweltering summer days. But the bruise itself is not dangerous. It is just unsightly.

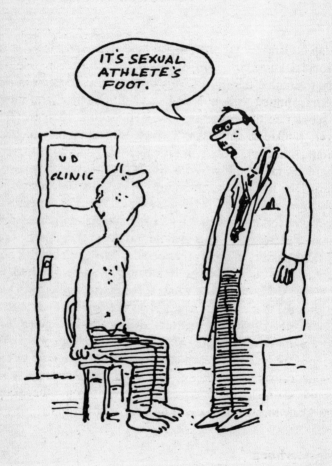

10 *Clap*

Clap is slang for VD or Venereal Diseases. And these, as you probably know, are diseases which are passed from one person to another during sex. Very occasionally, certain sorts can be transmitted without actual sexual intercourse, and there's a section on these diseases at the end of this chapter. However, nookie is the usual way of spreading the infection. Gonorrhoea and syphilis are the most famous sorts of VD, but there are many milder forms which are not as widely known, but which are just as important. All the different sorts of VD which we will discuss in this chapter can be very dangerous if they are left untreated. It is also important to have them treated *immediately*. They will not go away by themselves and you can pass them on to other people. At the back of this book is a list of useful addresses. Remember, no-one will think you are stupid if you are concerned about your health and ask questions; that is what these places are for.

VD is the side of sex that nobody likes to think about. One of the most relaxing benefits of a relationship where two people are faithful to each other is that they have no worries about 'catching something'. But even those malaises – like cystitis – which are not necessarily caught from other people are likely to put some strain on your relationship.

Gonorrhoea

The symptoms of gonorrhoea are often much more obvious in men than in women. In men, they appear about five to ten days after infection. Weeing becomes painful and a yellowish-white discharge seeps from the tip of the penis. A woman may not have any symptoms at all, although perhaps she may notice a change in her vaginal discharge or experience some discomfort when weeing. The only certain way of making sure a woman does or does not have gonorrhoea is to examine 'smears', which must be done by a special clinic. Most general hospitals have 'special clinics', which is a nice name for clap clinics.

The disease is treated with a course of antibiotics and it is best to stop drinking completely while you are taking them. If the disease is ignored, it can spread. Severe inflammation of the urethra can lead to a stricture, and if the infection spreads throughout the reproductive system, sterility may result. The further complications that can result from untreated gonorrhoea include septicaemia, peritonitis, conjunctivitis of the eyes and arthritis. So if you're worried, go for a check-up. Remember, a dose of gonorrhoea frequently recurs, so it is necessary to complete follow-up visits, particularly if the medicines prescribed are not taken absolutely religiously.

Syphilis

Again, this disease is easier to diagnose in men than in women. The first symptom is usually a chancre, or sore – a round, hollow lesion – which appears on the penis at or near the end between nine and ninety days after infection. This can also appear in the mouth, on the anus, the labia and the cervix. It is painless, and disappears spontaneously and quite quickly. This can lead some people to believe that there is nothing really wrong with them, but the disease then goes on to a much more serious stage. Like all clap, the earlier it is treated, the easier your recovery will be.

The secondary stage, after the sore – which some people never spot – occurs six to eight weeks after the appearance of the chancre. You may get symptoms such as headaches, rashes, swollen glands and intermittent fevers. Your hair may start to fall out and you will feel generally tired. About 75% of sufferers may get small ulcers in their mouths, or flat wart-like growths which appear on their genitals. These are highly infectious because they contain large numbers of bacteria which can be transmitted through kissing or sexual inter-course. This second stage is usually followed by a long time when you have no symptoms and whatever was wrong with you seems to have disappeared. This can go on from two to ten years.

In the third stage the disease begins to attack the skin, the mucous membranes and the long bones. It eventually spreads to the central nervous system, and can lead to madness because of the degeneration of the brain and the spinal cord.

Syphilis is diagnosed by a blood test, which is a routine test at your clap clinic, whatever you may think is wrong with you. In fact, syphilis is now quite a rare disease, thanks to medical advances, and much more common in homosexuals. In the first two stages, the disease can be cured by large injections of penicillin. In the third stage, it is possible only to slow down its progress. In the old days, arsenic was the cure.

Herpes

What is herpes? Herpes is a virus and there are two strains, Type 1 and Type 11. Type 1 is usually found in spit and causes cold sores. Type 11 is usually found in genital secretions and can cause painful blisters on the buttocks, vulva and vagina or on the cervix, where it can go unnoticed, or on the man's penis. Both types of herpes can be trans-mitted to other parts of the body, particularly as a result of oral sex. Herpes is probably the sexually-transmitted disease which worries people most as it has no absolute cure, and can recur for the rest of your life when your defences are down or if you are depressed.

151

The first bout of herpes is called the primary infection, and it is usually the most painful. The symptoms include a feeling of not being well, a fever, and losing your appetite. You may get tender, enlarged glands near the infected site, i.e. your neck or your groin. Once the attack is over, the virus persists in the latent state during which time you cannot give it to anyone.

No-one has yet found out what triggers off the next bout, but a wide variety of stressful situations can be the cause. They include sunburn, a fever, a bad cold or flu, being tired, sexual intercourse, pregnancy, your period and being upset about something. Herpes can come again because you are worrying a great deal about when you are going to get your next flare-up, which starts a vicious circle of worry and attacks. Herpes sufferers must learn, even more than others, to relax.

Is it dangerous? It is very worrying for a woman who is expecting a child. If a woman is having an attack of herpes when she is about to go in to labour, doctors will normally give her a caesarean. And she should tell her doctor, pregnant or not, if she has had outbreaks of either sort of herpes virus.

Is there a cure? There is no absolute cure for herpes, but there has been recent success with anti-viral drugs which your doctor or special clinic may be prescribing. But doctors also suggest warm baths to cleanse and soothe your skin (though some doctors favour showering, as they feel baths can spread the virus). Most doctors recommend that blisters be kept clean and dry so even if you do have a bath the infected area should be thoroughly dried afterwards and the towel put through the wash immediately.

Chlamydia

A chlamydia infection is caused by a microorganism that, just to be difficult, has some of the characteristics of a virus and some of a bacterium. It usually lodges first in the cervix (the neck of the womb) before it spreads to the uterus and the Fallopian tubes. Identification of chlamydia is a relatively recent medical discovery, and the symptoms may be difficult to spot. One indication that it may be present is a cystitis (urine) infection that is not responding to the usual treatment. It often goes hand in hand with gonorrhoea.

A test for chlamydia should also be performed if, during a routine pelvic examination, your doctor notices that your cervix is inflamed as this is a common symptom. It is important to detect and treat chlamydia because, like gonorrhoea, it can cause an infection of the uterine lining and the Fallopian tubes which can ultimately lead to scarring of the tubes and possible sterility. Active chlamydia in a woman who is giving birth can cause a severe eye infection and possible blindness in her baby. Tetracycline is the drug that cures chlamydia. Your sexual partner must also be treated even if he has no symptoms. Symptoms in men are usually 'non-specific urethritis', or a burning sensation on weeing, and he will reinfect you if he is not treated too.

Trichomonas

This infectious disease may be transmitted through sex but not exclusively so. It is a benign but again irritating infection. Men rarely experience symptoms, but women will often get a grey, foul-smelling discharge, often in huge quantities, which is usually accompanied by irritation and a lot of itching. It is easily treated with a drug called metronidazole but sometimes difficult to distinguish from gonorrhoea because often the two germs responsible for these illnesses can co-exist.

Aids

AIDS (Acquired Immune Deficiency Syndrome) is, in comparison to gonorrhoea and syphilis, a relatively new disease, and its sudden discovery has partly caused the recent surge of mass hysteria. Since AIDS *is* such a new disease, and medical researches and break-throughs are occurring continually, it would be wrong and probably misleading for me to describe its causes and results in any detail. One thing is certain though, it does mean that, today, young people have to be far more careful about their sexual partners. AIDS can only be passed on through vaginal or anal intercourse with an infected person. It can not be spread through kissing, sneezing, damp towels, jacuzzis, swimming pools, or by shaking hands. But people do not have to have AIDS symptoms in order to be infectious. Various clinics have been established to treat AIDS sufferers and to investigate the disease, and these are listed at the back of this book.

While nobody should allow the fear of AIDS to worry them to the extent that they cannot enjoy a normal life, it is still another reason why people should be careful about their choice of partners.

Crabs

Crabs are small, black creepy-crawlies, a bit like head lice, which you get in your pubic hair, although very occasionally you can get them in your eyebrows and eyelashes. You know you've got them because they itch like mad and you can see them running around in the hair. Crabs are distressing because they are extremely embarrassing. And although you can go to your chemist and ask the pharmacist for a lotion which will get rid of them, most people are too embarrassed in case anyone overhears them.

Crabs will not go away if you pick them off with tweezers as they will have laid eggs all over your pubic region. Nor will frantic attempts to shave your entire body, as a friend of mine did, do any good. The only way to get rid of crabs is with a special liquid, which you will be able to get from your doctor or alternatively, if you prefer to feel more anonymous, your local special clinic. Crabs are quite catching and it is not necessary to sleep with someone to get them. So while you have them, you should take care to use your own towel, pyjamas and bed.

Thrush

This is also known as candidiasis or moniliasis, and is caused by a yeast-like fungus. It won't kill you or cause permanent damage, but it might drive you to distraction as it is very uncomfortable. A huge number of women have suffered from it, and it is one of the most common complaints that women go to doctors about. It is not necessarily sexually transmitted, and frequently occurs because of some change in the vagina's flora and fauna – for instance, after taking a course of antibiotics – and because the organism can exist for a time outside the body, thrush can even be passed on by a damp towel.

Other factors that make you prone to the infection include diabetes, being fat, wearing nylon tights or underwear or very tight jeans, bubble baths, and certain women are prone to it during their pregnancies. Washing your fanny with soap can also upset its natural balance – warm water is quite sufficient to get you clean.

Thrush can infect the vagina or penis and less commonly, the mouth or rectum as well. Symptoms are a burning, itching sensation, along with a white curdy discharge that can look almost like cottage cheese. Intercourse may be painful and the vagina may turn from its usual pale pink to a bright red. Treatment is normally a supply of suppositories and cream. The usual dosage is two suppositories or two applications of cream every day for two weeks. Sex should be avoided during any treatment for infection and until you have got the all-clear from your doctor.

Cystitis

Most women at some point in their lives experience cystitis or some kind of urinary tract infection. There are many ways that bacteria can get into the urinary tract in the first place. Poor hygiene habits is one way (wiping from back to front instead of the other way round, for example), and intercourse is another. One type of bladder infection has been dubbed 'honeymoon cystitis' because in the past, women often experienced this for the first time on their honeymoons. Nowadays it is still common after your first sexual experience.

During sex, especially if the man is on top, the action of the penis against the vagina can irritate the overlying urethra and bladder structures as well as pushing bacteria from the vagina into the woman's urethral opening. Frequent shagging over a short period of time or if your vagina is not well lubricated will make the problem worse. Not all cystitis is caused by infection, therefore recurrent cystitis can come about because of this 'bruising' of the vaginal area and some women are anatomically prone to getting it. An ill-fitting diaphragm may also be a cause of recurrent infection because it will press on the neck of the bladder. During intercourse the back and forth action of the diaphragm rim, if it is too tight, will irritate and cause swelling. Then you have to leave your diaphragm in place for six to eight hours, and during these crucial hours, when the body's defence mechanism should be flushing out the bacteria that may have got into your bladder during sex, they are instead trapped there, as the too large diaphragm alters and restricts the flow of widdle by as much as 40%. Hence, if you have a cap and you have a recurrent problem, you may need to get a smaller diaphragm or switch to another method of birth control.

Having cystitis feels like you are weeing glass. Not only is there the painful, burning sensation when weeing, there is a difficulty in doing it and a need to do it every few minutes. All of this is likely to render a normally calm person completely hysterical, and it is incredibly debilitating as it often starts up at night and combines pain with exhaustion and sometimes panic. It is also combined with pain in the lower back, and tenderness in the lower tummy.

These infections can spread to the kidneys. The signs of a kidney infection will be more pronounced, including chills, fever, being sick and a very bad lower back ache. A swift course of antibiotics will clear it all up very quickly, but you must continue the course until long after the pain has gone away or, sure as eggs is eggs, it will be back for more torture. The best cure for urinary tract infections is generally believed to be prevention. Some women are prone to frequent attacks and they must learn a programme of 'self-help' to minimise these.

WHAT YOU CAN DO IF YOU ARE CYSTITIS-PRONE

1 Drink lots of fluid – not alcohol, which many women find, even in small doses, can provoke attacks – eight to ten glasses of water, lemon barley water or other soft drinks per day. (No tea or coffee.) This liquid helps flush bacteria out of your urinary tract.

2 Since the bacteria will flourish when stored in the urine inside your bladder, wee when you need to and don't try to hold on to it. Try to wee directly before and just after sex (in the loo not on the bed). It's important to resist the temptation to roll over and go to sleep – you may well wake up at three a.m. with cystitis instead.

3 Strange as this sounds, several girls I know who get frequent cystitis, get bouts after having very cold feet or walking on wet pavements. So try to keep your feet warm, and if you do have an attack, put on some warm socks. It really works for some people and coping with cystitis means finding out what works for you.

157

4 Drink a glass of cranberry juice in the morning and evening. Most of the bacteria that cause cystitis cannot survive in the acid environment created by the juice. This won't work for everyone but it's worth having a go.

5 When you shower, wash and rinse the vaginal and rectal areas well, and be sure to wipe from front to back after going to the bathroom. Avoid soap.

6 When you and your boyfriend make love, you can prevent infection-provoking irritation by using a lubricant. It is also especially important that he waits until you are ready.

7 Have the size of your diaphragm checked for fit, just in case.

8 Experiment with other positions which may not put so much pressure on your bladder.

COPING WITH A BOUT OF CYSTITIS

If you have cystitis, call your doctor and get an appointment as soon as possible. Doctors are very sympathetic about girls suffering from this as it is a very common and very upsetting problem. He will no doubt try to fit you in early on. Until you are able to see him, start to flush out the bacteria by drinking lots and lots of water. This will also give you something to wee – agony as it is, and much as you may want to wee as little as possible, it is less painful the more wee you have. Aspirin or an aspirin substitute may alleviate a little of your pain, and it is very comforting to clutch a hot water bottle as it relaxes the area.

Once your doctor has prescribed medication, your symptoms should clear up in about a day but whatever you do, do not stop taking your medicine or else you'll get it back again, and worse.

If you are plagued by repeated bouts of cystitis, you may get your doctor to pass you on to a urinary tract specialist for a check-up. If nothing is found, you may have chronic cystitis and your doctor may suggest you take an antibiotic on a regular basis. Many women object to this. Instead, they prefer to 'treat themselves'. Recurrent cystitis sufferers often carry around with them one of the proprietary brands of cystitis remedies such as Cystopurin and Cymalon, which can be bought at any local chemist. But if you are suffering for the first time, go to the doctor as it is important that he establishes there is an infection rather than just irritation or bruising.

HOW TO AVOID VD

1 Know your partner. If you are involved in a steady relationship with only one man, you are far less likely to ever contract a sexual disease – provided he is equally faithful to you.

2 Check them out. Examine prospective partners for genital sores or signs of a discharge. Don't have sex with him or her if anything looks unpleasantly suspicious to you.

3 Anyone who changes partners frequently should have periodic VD check-ups to make sure nothing has happened that they do not know about.

What happens at a VD clinic

These clinics, which you can find in your telephone directory under the name of your local hospital (look for the 'Special Clinic' number), are very discreet. You ring up for an appointment, and a nurse asks you for your name when you arrive. Then you will be asked to wait in a room of people who also look comfortingly nervous and as if they would rather be sitting an Advanced Mathematics A Level than waiting in this room. When the time comes, you will see the

159

doctor, who will ask some questions about your recent sexual history, i.e. when you last had sex, was it with somebody you knew well, is there a chance they could have had an infection, etc. A nurse will take a blood test and you will be asked for a urine sample. Then you will be examined by the doctor and various smears will be taken. In boys, this involves gently inserting a metal instrument up the penis, and in girls, with the aid of a speculum, the doctor will take smears from your cervix, vagina and vulva, as well as inserting a gloved hand to feel for any swollen glands or other signs of infection. Meanwhile, you will be lying on your back staring at a strategically placed picture of kittens or the Greek Islands.

Nobody is going to make any moral judgments. They are concerned with controlling the spread of venereal disease and are grateful for people coming to them for treatment. You will be asked to wait in the waiting room again for the results of the preliminary tests. These are not 100% accurate but often infections do show up immediately under the microscope, and if there is something amiss the treatment can start straight away. You will be asked to come back in a week for the results of further tests.

One part of the process which can be very distressing is informing all your sexual contacts. If you prefer, the clinic will do this for you by sending them a small card requesting them to come for treatment. It is *incredibly* important to be honest. Sexual diseases are not something you can bury your head in the sand about; they do not go away of their own accord and you can affect someone else's fertility and long-term health by not informing them of anything you may have passed on.

If you require any treatment, you will be asked to return for subsequent follow-up visits to check that all traces of the infection are passed. If you have a regular sex partner, it is often essential for them to receive similar treatment, even if they are symptomless, as otherwise the infection can pass backwards and forwards between you.

Questions and answers

Q How can I check a man's penis for herpes?

A Discreetly examining a man's penis can be a good idea. As you begin foreplay, while the light is still on, try and gently squeeze his willie to test for a discharge that may be greenishly yellow. If you stroke his willie and you feel a bump that makes him wince, he may have an emerging herpes sore. If the bump is soft and doesn't hurt him when you touch it, it could be a scar from a sore which has already healed. On the other hand, a bump that is painless but hard may indicate an infectious and dangerous genital wart. If anything seems strange to you ask your lover what it could be and how he's planning to take care of the problem. Do not go ahead and have intercourse or perform oral sex; explain that you would like to postpone it until he has seen a doctor.

Q Could I catch a sexual disease and not know about it?

A Yes. In women, the early stages of many sexual diseases can be symptomless or very slight, but this does not mean that there is nothing wrong. Hopefully, any man who has passed on a sexual disease will have the good grace to tell you. If someone disappears from your life with not so much as another word and no apparent explanation, it is sometimes painfully true that they have passed on some infection and can't bring themselves to tell you. So if someone disappears and you have any doubt about his health, make an appointment at your nearest Special Clinic. Honesty between sexual partners is very important. No matter how embarrassing you might think it is, he is playing around with your future fertility if he fails to tell you about a sexual infection – all of which may seem rather unimportant to couples who spend a great deal of trouble trying not to get pregnant. You may think that your future fertility is not something you should be worried about now, but give it ten years and you could be frantic. Fear that you have caught something is the worst reason for not getting a check-up. No sexual disease clears up on its own, unlike colds and flu.

The symptoms are much easier to spot in boys, as they will usually get a discharge or spots on their willie to warn them if an infection is present. However, in some diseases, like chlamydia or trichomonas, men can harbour the disease but be symptomless. So if a girl tells you she has one of these infections, you should be treated as well or you'll pass it back and forwards or on to the next person you sleep with.

Q I am promiscuous. Does that make me more vulnerable to Pelvic Inflammatory Disease?

A The numbers of cases of Pelvic Inflammatory Disease (PID), which is inflammation of the internal sexual organs, is increasing at an alarming rate. It is true that a woman with many lovers obviously has a greater risk of catching something than someone who only sleeps with one man all the time. PID is not necessarily related to sex; the organisms which cause the inflammation can come from other sources. But frequent sex with many different partners does contribute to the spread of the disease, and because it has only mild symptoms in its early stages, they are often ignored and women don't go to the doctor until it has got quite bad. PID can cause scarring of the Fallopian tubes and make it very difficult for a woman to conceive a child. It can also, in a later stage, be very painful. PID is also linked with the IUD, which is one reason doctors do not like to prescribe it for single women, as they feel there is a greater chance of them catching an infection which might develop into PID if untreated.

You should try to keep alert to changes in your body. A persistent ache in your pelvis after your period, a little temperature, or tenderness on your tummy, could all be symptoms of PID. And it is always worth checking with the doctor, who will give you antibiotics to prevent the infection from travelling to your Fallopian tubes.

Q Can I get VD in my mouth from oral sex?

A Yes. The soft mucous skin inside your mouth is very similar to vaginal and penile tissue. Sexually transmitted bacteria can then grow very easily there. You can not only contract gonorrhoea in your mouth, which may resemble constant cold sores, but also yeast infections and herpes.

11 *Yet more horrible problems*

Teacher crushes

Some people find that rather than getting crushes on unobtainable pop stars, they get them on their teachers, of the same or opposite sex. These crushes are rather harder to handle than the sort of fantasies you might have about pop stars, because you know your teachers and you also probably see them almost every day. Often these crushes develop because you are growing quite naturally away from your parents but you still want to look up to and love an adult, and a teacher seems a safe choice. All of this is probably unconscious. Don't worry about it, it won't last.

Most teachers are used to crushes; they are an occupational hazard. But unless you want to create what could be a terrible situation for both yourself and your teacher, and probably your family and his family, you must never attempt to get closer to 'your' teacher than you would with any other teacher you might see each day, and who doesn't arouse these feelings. Some of them have been known to be tempted, although most of them simply regard their pupils as another generation and could never find them attractive.

Very, very occasionally, a teacher will make a pass at a pupil. If this happens, you must tell your parents or headmistress/headmaster at once.

Sexual harassment in the office

There are many forms of harassment that can occur in an office situation, from simple leering to some old fart that stands next to the coffee machine, constantly telling filthy jokes and pinching everyone's bum. In most instances, annoying as it is, this kind of harassment can often be fairly easily dealt with. You can try to ignore it (though this sometimes has the effect of inflaming the situation and making them go to even greater lengths to get your attention) or make a joke of it, which defuses the situation and may even make him feel rather silly. Or you can give him a quick smack in the face, which has an element of surprise that should deter him in future. Should he continue to harass you in a way that is making work difficult, you can always go to your superior and make an official complaint. This will almost certainly put him off. In some cases, it may be your superior, however, who is harassing you. And some girls even fear for their jobs if they do not submit to his wandering hands.

Unless you wish to have an affair with your boss – and you should always consider all the implications, such as the fact he is likely to be married – no-one should blackmail you with the threat of losing your job for even mild sexual favours. In the same way, very few people sleep their way successfully to the top, even if someone has suggested that you might get promotion or a better job by using your favours. Office relationships are very complicated. Even if it goes well for a while, there is always resentment when it is over and it is often the woman who leaves the job, not the man.

If you do not wish to have an affair with your boss, or anything else, there are ways of being diplomatic and telling him so. Try inventing a boyfriend (if you don't already have one) or even explaining to him that you value your working relationship with him too much to have anything standing in its way and you feel that a romantic situation would affect both of your working lives.

If he does sack you, you must go immediately to your Citizens' Advice Bureau who will explain about going to an industrial tribunal, to make a claim for unfair dismissal. Sacking on the grounds that they won't shag you is strictly not allowed by law, and regarded as sexual discrimination.

166

Flashers

Anywhere girls collect in numbers is likely to attract flashers and also peeping toms. Flashers want to expose their willies at girls and peeping toms want to watch girls undress, such as in a swimming pool changing-rooms. Both are illegal. And both are quite disturbing, because even though you may not be touched, women often still feel very threatened. The whole point, for most flashers, is to shock. They derive their pleasure out of the reaction they get when women and girls squeal or scream for help when they get their willie out.

When my best friend was at school, there was one flasher who occasionally turned up at the hockey pitch and would stick his willie through a convenient hole in the fence surrounding the grounds. One day, he finally got his come-uppance when one brave girl (centre forward), made her way over to the fence and grasped his knob firmly through the hole, trapping him while the very red-faced hockey mistress had to go to telephone for the police. She then had to hang on to the willie for a quarter of an hour while a panda car made its way to the scene of the crime, which just shows what hockey can do for your grip.

At my own school – an establishment mainly renowned for its two main rules: one was that two pairs of knickers were to be worn at all times, including a large, navy blue serge pair (with a pocket in them to hold 2p in case you were lost in town) and the other being part of the first fire regulation of the school, which was 'put on both pairs of knickers and your raincoat' – our gardener used to pay 50p for a glimpse of the navy blue drawers, although he was finally sacked when he was caught, rather bizarrely, leaving a used Durex on the head girl's bed.

As you can see from the hockey pitch event, the best thing to do in all these cases, if possible, is to remain calm. If it happens when you are not near other people, such as on a train or in a subway, it is best to try and get away as quickly as you can but making as little fuss as you can. You should then make your way as fast as possible to someone in authority, such as the station master, who will then get in touch with the police. It is a good idea, even though you are probably scared shitless, to try and take in what he looks like so that you will be able to give them some kind of description.

Married men

Married men have a habit of making even the most confident woman turn into something of a walking cliché. This is because it's one of those situations where nearly all married men say the same things, all the girls think the same things and in the end all the same things happen.

Married men inevitably say that their wives don't understand them, they haven't been sleeping together for ten years, they're not going to leave their wives until their children are grown up and they've never felt this way about another woman. Women, who would otherwise laugh out loud at their friends were they to volunteer this same information, believe them. And this can often lead to a miserable and lonely situation, as many women find themselves waiting for years for a married man to leave his wife, meanwhile wasting time when they could be finding a husband of their own.

The other problem with married men is simply one of logistics. The only time that they have available for you is the time they can spare between working hours and the hours that they spend with their wives and families. So not only do the girlfriends of married men find themselves waiting endlessly for something that might not happen, they also wait endlessly for the one thing that's bound to happen. One of the worst things about married men, though, is that rather than enjoying the rosy afterglow, he has to get up and go home to his wife. There is very little chance you will be able to spend whole nights together and have him whisk you up bacon and eggs in the morning. Girls who go out with married men end up being alone at Christmas and Easter, or waiting in by the telephone in case he manages to escape to make a call, and generally being very lonely most of the time.

On the other hand, you may be receiving the unwelcome attentions of a married man, such as through a babysitting job, that you absolutely do not want and feel very threatened by. The first thing to do is the most obvious and that's look for another babysitting job. The second is to take a friend babysitting with you, since there is safety in numbers and it's also less boring than babysitting on your own. Whatever you do, don't be blackmailed.

Rape

There has been a lot of publicity recently about the rise in the number of rape cases. It is hard to tell if this is a genuine rise, or has come about because the police these days are much more sympathetic to the victims of rape, and so more people feel they can report what has happened without in some way feeling that it is them that is on trial.

Rape is a very serious crime. It happens when a man has sexual intercourse (which could also include sodomy or oral intercourse) with a woman against her will. There may well be some form of violence used to try to get a woman to submit, or a weapon might be used to intimidate the victim into submission. Rape does not only happen between strangers; boyfriends have been known to rape their girlfriends, and recently a change in the law meant that a man could be accused of raping his wife. Any act of intercourse against a woman's will is rape.

It can be enormously emotionally distressing as well as frequently being a violent act, because rape is more an act of dominance, with all its inherent violence, than a sexual act.

If you are raped, there are many organisations who will give you assistance and subsequent counselling, and their names and phone numbers are in the back of this book. Also, if you are raped, you must remember that when you get home, do not take a shower or bath no matter how unclean you feel as this washes away much of the evidence that police can use to track down the rapist.

The first thing you should do once you are safely away from your attacker is to telephone the police. Nearly all police stations have women officers who are well used to dealing with rape victims shortly after the crime, and will be sympathetic to your needs and emotions at this difficult time. Nobody is going to point the finger of blame at you, and rape should be reported in every case rather than you trying to forget it, because rapists tend to be habitual and you could be preventing some other girl from going through the horrible events you have just experienced.

A doctor will examine you for forensic evidence, i.e. semen samples, which can be used to pinpoint your attacker. After this, you will be able to shower and get yourself clean, since one of the commonest feelings after rape is of being dirty. They'll also have spare clothes at the police station which you can use. You are bound to be in a very highly emotional state. Ask to telephone your parents or a friend who can come to be with you until the police have finished asking the questions necessary for them to pursue their enquiries. Your parents are also bound to have very strong feelings about what has happened. It is also very common for parents to want retribution for the rapist, have his guts for garters etc.

Being raped has an effect on every woman's sex life. It's very common not to want to make love for quite a long time afterwards, and you may experience nightmares and need counselling or to talk to other rape victims (there are many groups of these) to compare notes and help you get over this. The best thing is to talk about what has happened as much as possible and try to get it out of your system rather than bottle it up.

Incest and other abuse

Incest is when sex takes place between people who are very closely related either by marriage or by blood, i.e. father/daughter, brother/sister, mother/son, stepfather/stepdaughter. Sexual abuse also often involves people that a child or young person may know very well, such as an uncle or a person even linked with his or her school. It is thought that incest is much, much more widespread than even the appallingly high incidents which have been reported suggest. This is because incest victims are often too young and too frightened ever to report it. One of the commonest threats is that the perpetrator of the crime will kill the child if he tells. Children naturally are brought up to believe everything that their parents and other adults tell them and live in fear of these threats. According to experts in America, one in four girls and one in seven boys are or have been or will be sexually abused before the age of thirteen. The problem is massive and all the more frightening because it is largely a secret crime and frightens us all. This is not only because of the horror that any harm to a child or young person inspires in all of us, but also because it shakes the whole foundations of what family life is built on and what we perceive it as.

In the case of children, sexual molestation (rather than incest) can be guarded against by a parent explaining a few basic things. The basic rule is that there is a difference between a good touch and a bad touch. Experts teach young children that if an older, more powerful person touches you on the part of your body covered by your bathing suit, except for health reasons, you should say 'No' very loudly and tell someone. Experts also advise against telling children to be wary only of crazy people or weird people because children often take this kind of thing literally. Children should be prepared to understand that a normal-looking person or even someone they know (as it is in 85% of cases) could molest them. Most important of all, children should understand that if they tell you anything they will not be punished and you will still love them.

There is a general agreement amongst those people who work with abuse victims that children rarely lie about it or make stories up. However, abused children who have been threatened will often admit to what's happened but then not admit who did it.

Incest victims are also often worried that, by reporting the crime, either to the police, or to a teacher, or to their mothers, they will in some way break up the family. But it is of vital importance to anyone who is being abused within their family in any way to immediately tell. Incest is a crime that depends on the victim's utter terror and dependence. If anybody ever does something to you that you do not like or which frightens you, and then tells you that it is your little secret, they know that they are doing something very wrong. Incest victims not only suffer from the fear of what is happening to them (which is often worse, because they are led to believe that this is what all daddies/grandfathers/ brothers do to children), but they daren't tell anyone and they start to believe that they are a bad person because they brought it on themselves. Incest victims have enormous problems ever having a normal sex life; they also experience difficulties with schoolwork, trusting anyone, being friendly, they tend to suffer from serious depressions, dietary problems, drug taking and stealing. These can all be signs that incest is present within a family.

It is not just the sex involved that makes an incest victim feel loathsome and dirty. It is the fact that the one person in everyone's life that they should always be able to trust to love them unselfishly is abusing that trust and love for their own warped pleasure. Personally I think anyone who inflicts themselves on a young child in any way would be better off dead.

At the back of the book there are addresses of places and people to turn to who will give you advice no matter who it is who is abusing you. The Incest Crisis Line and various other groups will be kind, sympathetic and supportive. *They will also believe you.* They do not wish to break up anyone's family or destroy anyone's life, but they will do everything possible to support *you*.

Communications –
addresses/telephone numbers

Adoption Resource Exchange
11 Southwark Street, London SE1 1RQ.
Telephone: 01–407–8800

Al-Anon Family Groups UK & Eire
61 Great Dover Street, London SE1 4YF.
Telephone: 01–403–0888
Support group for families of alcoholics (24 hour service)

Alateen
61 Great Dover Street, London SE1 4YF.
Telephone: 01–403–0888.
Branch of **Al-Anon** for young people with alcoholic relatives

Alcohol Concern
305 Gray's Inn Road, London WC1X 8QF.
Telephone: 01–833–3471

Alcoholics Anonymous
Box 514, 11 Redcliffe Gardens, London SW10 9BQ.
Telephone: 01–352–9779

Anorexic Aid, Voluntary Self Help
Priory Centre, 11 Priory Road, High Wycombe, Bucks.

Anorexic Family Aid
c/o Catherine Wells, 43 Low Road, Hellesdon, Norwich NR6 5AE.

Anorexics Anonymous
45a Castelnau, London SW13.
Telephone: 01–748–3994

Ash (Action on Smoking and Health)
5–11 Mortimer Street, London W1 7RH.
Telephone: 01–637–9843

Association for Improvements in Maternity Services
163 Liverpool Road, London N1 0RF.
Telephone: 01–278–5628

Association of British Adoption and Fostering Agencies
11 Southwark Street, London SE1 1RQ.
Telephone: 01–407–8800

Bowman Society (Homosexuals, Transvestites, Transsexuals)
Box 3084, NC1N 8XX

British Association for the Study and Prevention of Child Abuse and Neglect
Jacobs Bright Children Centre, Whitworth Road, Rochdale, Lancs. OL12 6EP.
Telephone: 0706–56121

British Pregnancy Advisory Service (BPAS)
1st Floor, Guildhall Buildings, Navigation Street, Birmingham B2 4BT.
Telephone: 021–643–1461
Scotland:
2nd Floor, 245 North Street, Glasgow.
Telephone: 041–204–1832
Wales:
4 High Street, Arcade Chambers, Cardiff.
Telephone: 0222–372389

Brook Advisory Centres (Contraception, Abortion, Pregnancy)
233 Tottenham Court Road, London W1P 9AL.
Telephone: 01–580–2991/01–323–1522
Centres all around the country
Scotland:
2 Lower Gilmore Place, Edinburgh, EH3 9NY.
Telephone: 031–229–3596

Capital Helpline
Telephone: 01–388–7575

Citizens' Advice Bureau
London:
33 Charing Cross Road, London WC2H OAU.
Telephone: 01–839–2825
For information on other branches telephone: 01–251–2000
Scotland:
82 Nicolson Street, Edinburgh EH8 9EW.
Telephone: 031–667–0156
Northern Ireland:
Newforge Lane, Belfast BT9 5NW.
Telephone: 0232–681117

Department of Health and Social Security
Alexander Fleming House, Elephant and Castle, London SE1 6BY.
Telephone: 01–407–5522

Family Planning Association (FPA)
27–35 Mortimer Street, London W1A 4QW.
Telephone: 01–636–7866
Northern Ireland:
113 University Street, Belfast.
Telephone: 0232–225–488

Friend (Homosexuals, Transvestites, Transsexuals)
Telephone: 01–837–7324 evenings 7.30 pm–10.00 pm

Gingerbread (One Parent Families)
25 Wellington Street, London WC2E 7BN.
Telephone: 01–240–0953
Scotland:
39 Hope Street, Glasgow G3 7DW.
Telephone: 041–248–6840
Northern Ireland:
171 University Street, Belfast BT7 1HR.
Telephone: 0232–231417

Haemophiliac Society (AIDS)
PO Box 9, 16 Trinity Street, London SE1 1DE.
Telephone: 01–407–1010

Incest Crisis Line
32 Newbury Close, Northolt, Middlesex UB5 4JS
Telephone: 01–422–5100/01–890–4732

Incorporated Law Society of Northern Ireland
The Royal Courts of Justice, Chichester Street, Belfast BT1 3JS.
Telephone: 0232–235111

International Planned Parenthood Federation (IPPF)
Regent's College, Inner Circle, Regent's Park, London NW1 4NS.
Telephone: 01–486–0741

La Leche League (Breastfeeding)
Telephone: 01–883–7801

Law Society
113 Chancery Lane, London WC2A 1PL.
Telephone: 01–242–1222

Law Society of Scotland
26 Drumsheugh Gardens, Edinburgh EH3 7YR.
Telephone: 031–226–7411

Legal Action Group
242–244 Pentonville Road, London N1 9UN.
Telephone: 01–833–3931

Legal Aid
Contact either **Citizens' Advice Bureaux** or **Legal Aid Offices**

Life (Contraception, Abortion, Pregnancy)
118–120 Warwick Street, Leamington Spa, Warwicks. CV32 4QY.
Telephone: 0926–21587

Life (Free Pregnancy Testing)
57a London Road, West Croydon.
Telephone: 01–688–1985

Marie Stopes House
Appointments Secretary, Room 7, The Well Woman Centre, 108
Whitfield Street, London W1P 6BE.
Telephone: 01–388–0662

National Association for Maternal and Child Welfare
1 South Audley Street, London W1Y 6JS.
Telephone: 01–491–2772

**National Association of Young Persons Counselling and Advisory
Services (NAYPCAS)**
17–23 Albion Street, Leicester LE1 6GD.
Telephone: 0533–558763

National Childbirth Trust
9 Queensborough Terrace, Bayswater, London W2 3TB.
Telephone: 01–221–3833

National Childminding Association
8 Mason's Hill, Bromley, Kent BR2 9EY.
Telephone: 01–464–6164

National Council for One Parent Families
255 Kentish Town Road, London NW5 2LX.
Telephone: 01–267–1361

National Council for Voluntary Organisations
26 Bedford Square, London WC1B 3HU.
Telephone: 01–636–4066

National Federation of 18 Plus Groups
Nicholson House, Old Court Road, Newent, Gloucs. GL18 1AG.
Telephone: 0531–821210

National Federation of Solo Clubs
Ruskin Chambers, 191 Corporation Street, Birmingham B4 6KY.
Telephone: 021–236–2879

National Federation of Youth Clubs
2 Belvedere Place, Dublin 1.
Telephone: 0001–729933

National Foster Care Association
Francis House, Francis Street, Victoria, London SW1 1DE.
Telephone: 01–828–6266

National Society for the Prevention of Cruelty to Children (NSPCC)
67 Saffron Hill, London EC1N 8RS.
Telephone: 01–242–1626

Northern Ireland Council of Social Services
Newforge Lane, Belfast BT9 5NW.
Telephone: 0232–681117

Parents for Children
222 Camden High Street, London NW1 8QR.
Telephone: 01–485–7526/7548
Specialises in placing older and handicapped children/adoptions by single people

Rape Crisis Centre
P.O. Box 558, Birmingham B3 2HL.
Telephone: 021–233–2122
London:
P.O. Box 42, London N6 5BU.
Telephone: 01–837–1600

Release (Drug Addiction)
169 Commercial Street, London E1 6BW.
24 hour service. Emergency telephone: 01–603–8654 (ring first to make appointment)

Samaritans (Counselling)
Head Office, 39 Walbrook, London EC4 8BP.
Telephone: 01–283–3400 24 hour service

Scottish Adoption Association
69 Dublin Street, Edinburgh EH3 6NS.
Telephone: 031–556–2070

Scottish Council for Single Parents
13 Gayfield Square, Edinburgh EH1 3NX.
Telephone: 031–556–3899
Glasgow:
39 Hope Street, Glasgow G3 7DW.
Telephone: 041–248–3488
Dundee:
150 Haddington Crescent, Dundee DD4 0LZ.
Telephone: 0382–501–972

Silhouette Slimming Club Ltd
21 Rolle Street, Exmouth, Devon EX8 1HA.
Telephone: 0395–277725

Singles Society (Dateline)
23–25 Abingdon Road, London W8 6AH.
Telephone: 01–937–6503

Slimming Magazine and Slimming Clubs
Victory House, Leicester Place, London WC2H 7NB.
Telephone: 01–437–9011

Standing Conference on Drug Abuse (SCODA)
1–4 Hatton Place, Hatton Gardens, London EC1N 8ND.
Telephone: 01–430–2341

Terence Higgins Trust (AIDS)
Telephone: 01–833 –2971 Mon–Fri: 7.00 pm–10.00 pm/Sat–Sun: 3.00
pm–10.00 pm

Thomas Coram Foundation for Children
40 Brunswick Square, London WC1N 1AZ.
Telephone: 01–278–2424
Adoption and fostering care for children with special needs. Children day
care centre in London and over 50 mile radius.

Transsexual Action Group
BM Box 683, London WC1V 6XX.

TVTS Support Group (Homosexuals, Transvestites, Transsexuals)
Telephone: 01–729–1460. Tues, Wed, Thurs: 10.30 am–4.30 pm/Fri:
2.30 pm– 4.30 pm/Evenings: Fri, Sat, Sun: 8.00 pm–10.00 pm

Ulster Pregnancy Advisory Service
719a Lisburn Road, Belfast 9.
Telephone: 0232–667345

Weight Watchers UK Ltd
11–12 Fairacres, Dedworth Road, Windsor, Berks SL4 4UY.
Telephone: 0753–856751

Women Against Rape
71 Tonbridge Street, Camden Town, London WC1H 9DZ.
Telephone: 01–837–7509

Women's Aid
52–54 Featherstone Street, London EC1Y 8RY.
Telephone: 01–251–6537

Women's Aid Refuge National Office Number: 01–831–6537

The Women's Rape Action Group Number: 01–837–1600

Women's Therapy Centre
6 Manor Gardens, London N7 6LA.
Telephone: 01–263–6200

YMCA
640 Forest Road, Walthamstow, London E17 3DZ.
Telephone: 01–520–5599

Youth Hostels Association
Trevelyan House, Saint Stephens Hill, St Albans, Herts. AL1 2DY.
Telephone: 0727–55215

YWCA of Great Britain
Clarendon House, 52 Cornmarket Street, Oxford OX1 3EJ.
Telephone: 0865–726110